DICK WHITTINGTON

Illustrated by
Kathi Garry–McCord

Troll Associates

Library of Congress Cataloging in Publication Data

Whittington and his cat.
  Dick Whittington.

    SUMMARY: Retells the tale of the poor boy who
trades his beloved cat for a fortune in gold and
jewels and becomes Lord Mayor of London.
    1. Whittington, Richard, d. 1423—Juvenile
literature. [1. Whittington, Richard, d. 1423.
2. Folklore—England] I. Garry-McCord, Kathleen.
II. Title.
PZ8.1.W59Gar   398.2'1'0941   80-28171
ISBN 0-89375-482-X   AACR1
ISBN 0-89375-483-8 (pbk.)

10 9 8 7 6 5 4 3

DICK
WHITTINGTON

Long, long ago, a young boy named Dick Whittington
lived in England. He had no father and mother, so he
had to beg for food. Some days, he was lucky to get even
a crust of bread and some potato peelings.

Dick always listened when people spoke. So he had heard many strange stories about the wonderful city of London. In London, people sang all day long, and the streets were paved with gold.

One day, Dick heard a wagoner say that he was heading for London. So the boy decided that he would also go. It was a long journey, and Dick was tired when he finally reached the city. But he ran off at once to find the streets that were paved with gold. By nightfall, he had found nothing but dirt and common paving stones. Exhausted, he fell asleep in a dark corner.

When he awoke, it was morning, and he was very hungry. He asked everyone he met if they would give him some money for something to eat. But he got very little, and soon he grew weak.

One evening, Dick lay down in the doorway of Mr. Fitzwarren, a rich merchant. Mr. Fitzwarren's cook had a terrible temper. When she saw Dick, she cried, "Be off with you, or I will douse you with dishwater!"

At that very moment, Mr. Fitzwarren arrived. He ordered the servants to take Dick inside and give him a good meal. And when the boy was strong enough, he was given a job in the kitchen.

FOREWORD

When I first received the manuscript for Raymond Culpepper's book, *No Church Left Behind*, I treated it as just another request to write a foreword for a book. However, everything changed when I read how Raymond's terminally ill father made an urgent request: "Drive me back to the little country church in Grand Falls, North Carolina, where I was saved and preached my first sermon."

Again, this seemed like just another heartwarming story until I came to the punch line. That's when I realized the visit to that little church was not just for Raymond or his father; they went back for me—Elmer Towns. The story touched me spiritually, and it will touch you also. I cannot tell you the punch line; you have to read it for yourself. When you do, I hope God speaks to you as He spoke to Raymond and to me.

This is not your average book on church-growth principles, nor is it similar to a lot of new books by pastors who have discovered a "new way to do church growth." This book is about discovering the presence and power of God in your life and in your ministry. If that is what you want, then commit yourself to read every word.

Not many books are written with such passion and conviction. Many pastors are anointed to preach, but the anointing does not always carry over into their writing and the other aspects of their ministry. I believe God anointed Raymond Culpepper to write this book for pastors and church workers alike. Perhaps his father's prophetic words speak to you now: *Have you lost the edge? Have you lost heart? Is His anointing fresh? What about your first love?*

Over twenty-five years ago, Raymond Culpepper invited me to speak to Church of God congregations in Indiana, where he was state director of youth and Christian education. Later, he invited me to bring the same message to the churches in Alabama. At that point I said to Raymond, "You have something greater than just an administrative gift to run a state program—you have an anointing of God that could be used to build a *great* local church."

I reminded him that the greatest work for God is done through pastors and local churches. Those who work for the denominations in state and national offices only support the work of churches. My challenge to Raymond was to leave his state post, plant a church, and build it into a great church.

So in 1980 Raymond Culpepper began Metro Church of God in Birmingham, Alabama. Today there are 3,000 members and a huge complex of buildings on a campus that is valued at over $20 million.

I praise God for my friendship with Raymond Culpepper, and pray that you will catch his passion as you read this book.

—Elmer L. Towns
Cofounder, Liberty University
Dean, School of Religion
Lynchburg, Virginia

INTRODUCTION

In April 1984, my father was diagnosed with terminal cancer. Thirty brief and pain-filled days later, he died. He was only fifty-seven.

Within an hour of the oncologist's diagnosis, Dad said to me, "Son, I want you to drive me back to the little country church in Granite Falls, North Carolina, where I was saved, and preached my first sermon."

Desperately, I wanted to fulfill his desire, but Dad was terribly sick. His abdominal cavity would fill with fluid, requiring his doctor to drain it. His stomach would become distended up to 10 or 12 inches before each draining. The pain was unbearable. The vomiting was continual, the suffering unspeakable.

Every few days he would say, "We have to go back to my 'Bethel,' Son, and you have to take me." As much as I wanted to go, I knew he did not have the strength to make the trip. He was so weak we had to lift him from his bed and chair, and assist him with personal hygiene.

About two weeks after his first request to go back to his Bethel, he announced, "Tomorrow we are leaving for North Carolina." I tried to convince him otherwise, but he would not hear of postponing the trip any longer.

So the next day we went by the doctor's office to have the fluid drained; then we left Atlanta, Georgia, for Granite Falls, North Carolina. We had traveled only about two and a half hours before his stomach filled with fluid again, and he became extremely ill.

We were forced to stop at a department store and buy a larger pair of trousers—from size 36 to size 48 waist. It was obvious he could not go on, so I rented a motel room for what would be a most difficult night.

Fever, vomiting, and dry heaves were unrelenting that night. All I could do was pray, wipe his dehydrated lips with a damp cloth, and wonder why he stubbornly persisted in making such an awful journey. It was the most challenging trip I have ever made in my life.

PILGRIMAGE TO NORTH CAROLINA

The next morning I begged him to return to his doctor in Atlanta, but he would not surrender. "We are going," he insisted repeatedly. "We must go!"

Six grueling hours later we drove into the small community of Granite Falls, near Hickory, North Carolina. He had not been back in thirty-four years. He observed that everything looked almost the same. As we walked slowly toward the little brick Church of God building, Dad rehearsed his story for me.

> It was Sunday afternoon when I found this church. I had been drinking heavily since the Wednesday night before. Early that Sunday morning, the Lord spoke to me and convicted my heart. I knew I had to get saved.

> I drove for hours, sobering up and humming a song I had heard my mother sing. I didn't know the song, but later I learned it was "The Old Rugged Cross."

I listened quietly while he related the story, as we entered the building through a basement door. Walking down a narrow hallway for perhaps 30 feet, Dad motioned toward a classroom on the right and said, "That's the very room where God gave me my first sermon from 1 Corinthians 13." Tears filled his eyes.

> I had been saved only three weeks, and baptized in the Holy Ghost only six days, but I knew I was called to preach the Gospel. I didn't know anything about the Bible or preaching; but I told God if He would help me just one time, I would never doubt my calling again.

Spontaneously, Dad gave thanks to God and broke into a prayer. I watched him clap his hands for joy, then raise them to God in worship. I felt like an intruder. I did not know how to act or what to say. I watched in awestricken silence.

A few minutes later we cautiously navigated our way up a flight of narrow steps and into a small sanctuary. Dad observed that the paint, carpet, and furniture were different. With a note of triumph, he announced, "But this is the place!"

With that, his index finger aimed at a single spot, and he exclaimed, "Son, that's where your old daddy got saved!" Tears coursed down his sunken cheeks. He slowly walked to the spot and dropped to the floor on his knees.

He thanked God for salvation, his wife, his mother, his children, and thirty-four years of divine faithfulness. He thanked God for the Church of God and God's call on his life. I had never seen my father worship like he did that day. The presence of the Holy Spirit refreshed his frail body with new strength. Before my eyes, he became a strong man of God on a mission.

Suddenly, Dad stopped praying, stood up, reached toward the pulpit and took a bottle of anointing oil in his hand. I was not prepared for what followed. "Son," he began. "I did not ask you to bring me here just for myself. *I came to bring you!*"

For several minutes, face-to-face and eye-to-eye, he opened my heart and revealed its contents. His words burned! He had never talked to me quite like that before.

> Son, you have lost the edge. You began as a pastor with a big dream, but it has been rough. Your heart is beaten up. You're discouraged. You are busy, but not very effective. You have learned how to act like a preacher, but you're empty.

His words were poignant.

You've lost your burden for lost people. Your prayer life is in trouble. No tears punctuate your preaching. You're not hungry for God like you used to be. You know how to say the right things and push the right buttons; but like Samson who shook himself, you don't know the Spirit is gone.

The anointing is not fresh. Your fire has gone out. You have left your first love. You must get the edge back!

Without another word, Dad anointed my head with oil. Laying his holy hands on my head, he prayed:

God, forgive my son. He has grown cold. He is trying to do Your work in the flesh and has forgotten it is not by might or by power, but by Your Spirit. His anointing is not fresh. His burden for lost people is gone. Don't let him waste his precious life or Your divine calling by just going through the motions. Revive my boy in the midst of his years. Give him back his edge.

His face was soaked with tears when he finally said "Amen." "Promise me," he demanded. "Promise me you'll repent, pray through, and get your heart right! I cannot leave this place today until you promise me."

I felt exposed, embarrassed, convicted. There I was . . . a husband, father, pastor, and leader being told I had lost my heart for God and for His cause. The truth hurt.

"Yes, sir," I said, "I promise." It was a promise that changed my life.

Two weeks later, Dad rested from his labors and stepped into the presence of Jesus.

Since this book is about the local church, you may wonder why I share this experience from more than twenty-three years ago. Why do I begin with the story of a dying father's message to his son who was unconsciously drifting?

It is simply because any discussion about a local church being left behind is ludicrous unless individuals have an edge. Without a burden, a fresh anointing, repentance, and first-love commitment, a book like this is just another collection of thoughts, passively read and soon forgotten.

Maybe this experience was not for me only. Perhaps it was for you, too. Can the words of a dying preacher in 1984 speak to the twenty-first-century Church? My dad's words not only indicted me then, their prophetic message is also relevant to the Church today.

Has the twenty-first-century Church lost its edge? Have we been mesmerized by the world's system? Have the years, tears, jeers and sneers put out the fire on our altars? Have we come to the place where we think we can push the right buttons, play the expected games, say the acceptable things and still impact our communities?

I cannot help but wonder what would have happened to me if Dad had not performed "open-heart surgery" on me that day. Perhaps those prophetic words will speak to you now. God has promised:

"I will give you a new heart and put a new spirit within you; I will take the heart of stone out of your flesh and give you a heart of flesh. I will put My Spirit within you and cause you to walk in My statutes, and you will keep My judgments and do them. Then you shall dwell in the land that I gave to your fathers; you shall be My people, and I will be your God" (Ezek. 36:26-28).

Here is the burning truth: If you lose your edge, your church will be left behind . . .

- *Left behind in the mission of evangelizing the lost.* We live in a world where communication is fast . . . and becoming less expensive every day.

- *Left behind while the last-days Pentecostal revival sweeps the globe.*

- *Left behind in the quest to impact families and communities.* Involvement in the community is more important to a church than image and buildings.

- *Left behind in growth and maturity.* Some churches have been in existence a long time, but they foster unhealthy attitudes and practices.

- *Left behind in fulfilling the destiny God has promised.* The bold promise made in Jeremiah 29:11 is as applicable to a church as it is to an individual:

  "For I know the plans I have for you," declares the Lord, "plans to prosper you and not to harm you, plans to give you hope and a future" (NIV).

Perhaps my father's prophetic words speak to you now: *Have you lost the edge? Have you lost heart? Is His anointing fresh? What about your first love?*

You and I are about to embark on a journey, but without a renewed edge of the Holy Spirit, it will be a treadmill to nowhere. We will find ourselves recycling entrenched, ineffective thinking; pushing buttons; playing games and filling roles.

As I share my heart with you, my sincere prayer is that *no church will be left behind*!

Chapter 1

No Church Left Behind

On January 8, 2002, the president of the United States signed into law the *No Child Left Behind Act of 2001* (NCLB). This Law focused on helping every primary and high school student in America achieve grade level in his or her school.

The program's blueprint was based on four foundational principles: accountability, flexibility of resources, proven methods, and choices for parents. It was a bold experiment for education. Five years later, the impact of NCLB was undeniable, and Congress renewed the legislation. Newspapers across the country, including the *San Francisco Chronicle* and the *Spartanburg Herald-Journal*, trumpeted the effectiveness and success of NCLB in their editorials.

If children were being left behind in the educational system of our country, what about the churches that are being left behind in the greatest enterprise of the ages? We are called to worship God passionately, to evangelize the whole world, and to disciple and equip believers for service.

Too many churches in America, however, are marginalized by low ministry expectations, basic biblical illiteracy, and paralyzing self-doubt. In a constantly changing world that requires increasingly innovative ministries and complex cultural and physical adaptations, churches are literally being left behind. Some congregations are preaching and teaching the Gospel . . . but they are reaching no one. What can we do?

People talk about a "great church." A great church has nothing to do with the number on its membership roll, but it has everything to do with the quality of its ministry. Great churches are not about bricks, budgets, buildings, and business. Great churches are about our great Savior . . . knowing Him and making Him known. They are about being and doing what God has called them to be and do.

I have been privileged to serve in a local church setting for more than twenty-five years. I have seen the church up close and personal. I do not pretend I have seen it all, but I have seen some good, some bad, and some ugly.

Some of the Good

- Seeds growing and harvests reaped
- Disciples committed and saints who are loyal

- Great leaders and exemplary followers
- Sacrificial givers and Kingdom builders
- Churches planted and communities transformed
- Healthy churches with Christ exalted
- Sinners saved and homes healed

Some of the Bad

- Unheeded warnings and Christ rejected
- Broken homes and tragic stories
- Prodigal children and heartbroken parents
- Unanswered questions and empty answers
- Sinners saved and never discipled
- Dead traditions and religious fads
- Audacious beginnings and burned-out endings

Some of the Ugly

- Power struggles and church politics
- High expectations and low commitment
- Personal sacrifices and ungrateful responses
- Stifling legalism and false doctrines
- Churches dying and self-centered agendas
- Character assassinations and wounded warriors
- Visions victimized and dreams dead

Because of the good and despite the bad and the ugly, I am passionate about the Church. I believe the Church is the last, best, and only hope for America. It is the Church, or it's lights out for us all. When the Church is clicking, it's living up to its God-given mission . . . and there's nothing like it on earth!

When I detect the aspiration to greatness in a congregation, I am thrilled. Personally, I am passionate about the health, strength, and future of local congregations. Regardless of size and situations, every church can be a great church. No church should be left behind.

THE GOOD NEWS FIRST

There is good news and bad news. The good news is the Church is alive and thriving outside America. In *Mega Shift: Igniting Spiritual Power*, James Rutz says:

- In 1960, Western Evangelicals outnumbered non-Western Evangelicals (mostly Latinos, blacks, and Asians) by 2 to 1. By 2000, non-Westerners had pulled ahead by 4 to 1. It is projected that by 2010, the ratio will be 7 to 1.

- In Latin America, more Evangelicals attend church on Sunday morning than Catholics.

- There are more missionaries from non-Western nations than from Western nations.

- Around the world, 3,000 people are saved every twenty-five minutes. This means that every twenty-four hours, there are 175,000 new believers in 238 nations.

- In 1960, there were twenty-four nonbelievers for every believer in the world; today there are only six.
- Every month, five million new believers are added to Christ's body around the world.
- Between 1990 and 2004, Christians in Cambodia grew from 200 to 400,000.
- The population of Guatemala is now 44 percent born-again Christians. Neighboring El Salvador is 53.6 percent Christian.
- In 1981, Rio de Janeiro had thirty spiritist centers for each Evangelical church. By 1996, the number had reversed to forty Evangelical churches for each spiritist center.
- Approximately 25,000 house churches were started in India in the year 2002.
- More Muslims have turned to Christ in the past ten years than in the previous 1,000 years.
- In 1970, Nepal had 5,200 Christians. In 2000, there were over 540,000 believers.
- The Evangelical church in Laos grew from 32,000 to 80,000 in three years.
- From 1992 to 1997, Christians among the Pygmies in the Congo grew from almost none to 300,000.
- Zimbabwe added 6,000 new churches from 1992 to 1998 and 2,240,000 new believers.
- Today, China has 115 million to 120 million believers, the world's largest national church. China also has roughly one million active church planters.

- In 1970, there were 45 million Charismatics and Pentecostals in the world. By 2000, there were 447 million; by 2005, there were 650 million. Pentecostals grew at 8.8 percent annually; Evangelicals grew at 1.1 percent annually.[1]

THE BAD NEWS

Unfortunately, the American church is losing influence. In 1998, George Barna wrote:

> The church in America is losing influence and adherents faster than any other major institution in the nation. . . . The typical church as we know it has a rapidly expiring shelf life. . . . At the risk of sounding like an alarmist, I believe the church in America has no more than five years . . . to turn itself around and begin to affect the culture, rather than be affected by it.[2]

Sadly, America is closing her churches. Lyle Schaller, prominent church-growth scholar, says we are closing thirty-seven churches every day in America. That's 13,505 a year. We plant fourteen churches per day, or 5,110 a year. The net loss for Christian churches in America is 8,395 annually.

Alarmingly, the United States population is outgrowing our churches. The Gallup organization reveals the following:

Year	Churches per 1,000 people
1900	27
1950	17
1980	12
1996	11

The North American Society for Church Growth agrees. This organization says that Evangelical churches in the U.S. have failed to gain even 2 percent of the population in the past fifty years. Sadly, we are not even reaching our children.

Regrettably, church membership is declining in America. The Institute of American Church Growth's Dr. Charles Arn says, "Combined membership of all Protestant denominations (in the U.S.) has declined 9.5 percent in the last ten years while the population has grown by 11 percent."

Arn goes on to report that not a single county in America has a higher percentage of churched people than it did ten years ago.

Understandably, American pastors are feeling the pressure. H. B. London with *Focus on the Family* pointed out that . . .

- 45 percent of pastors suffer from burnout
- 90 percent say they were not properly trained to handle the multiple demands of ministry
- 70 percent have a lower self-esteem than when they entered the ministry
- 95 percent struggle with discouragement
- 80 percent say ministry negatively affects their family
- 70 percent of pastors say they have no close friends.[3]

Alarmingly, believers in America are dropping out of church. According to Barna's findings, 40 percent of adults say they are church members, but only 20 percent attend services.

The story is better in the Church of God (Cleveland, Tennessee), but it is still challenging. Dr. R. Wallace Sibley, international director of Evangelism and Home Missions, recently shared a study with me:

- In the past ten years, U.S. membership has shown a net increase.

- The number of churches planted in that period was 3,677.

- The number of churches closed from 1984 to 2004 was 2,439.

- Net gain in new churches organized was 1,233.

This study shows a *net gain* of sixty-one churches per year in the fifty states. The average net gain is 1.2 churches per year, per state.

Will Christianity in America follow the path of historic decline that Europe traveled? At one time, 70 percent of some European nations were Christian. Today, those same nations are only 2 or 3 percent Christian.

Our hope—great churches. The solution isn't up to Christ; it's our move!

CAESAREA PHILIPPI REVISITED

The first reference Jesus made to the Church is recorded in Matthew 16. After preaching for three years of public ministry, He was approaching the last six months of His earthly life.

Jesus knew He was facing the Cross. With questions, confusion, and rejection swirling around Him, He led His disciples to the region of Caesarea Philippi (today's Golan Heights).

Look at a map of Israel. Study the footsteps of Jesus and you will discover that this was a very unusual visit to Caesarea Philippi. In fact, there were several firsts associated with this trip:

- The first and only time Jesus visited Caesarea Philippi
- The first time He asked the disciples if they really understood His identity
- The first time Jesus announced His death to the disciples
- The first time the word *church* was used in the New Testament

The region was both symbolic and significant. It was symbolic because it represented the antithesis of everything Jesus personified. It was significant because Jesus chose to announce His agenda in enemy territory. Note how this geographical region, or territory, was marked by at least five characteristics.

1. Idolatry

The region had been a stronghold of Baal worship in the seventh century BC. On the hillsides of this region the ancient Assyrians built no less than fourteen temples dedicated to Baal, who was known as the god of strong storms and fertility. The area had been a center of Baalism, which included base sexual worship, religious prostitution, and human sacrifice.

A particularly odious practice in the seventh century BC was to kill young children and bury them in the foundations of houses or public buildings. This was an idolatrous effort to curry the favor of their gods. The regional culture was overrun with idolatry.

2. Mythology

The city of Caesarea Philippi was also a cult center dedicated to the worship of Pan. Greek legend has it that the mythological god, Pan, was born in a cave in this region. In fact, before Herod's son, Philip, named the city Caesarea Philippi, it was called Panias. Today it is known as Banias.

The myths caricatured Pan as half-goat and half-man. The Greeks even built a temple dedicated to Pan worship. The son of the Greek god Hermes, Pan was celebrated as the god of wild nature, herdsmen, and music.

3. Immorality

Both idolatrous Baal worship and Pan mythology were immoral to the core. Baalism spawned fertility cults that were active during Christ's visit to the region. Pan was well known as a patron of homosexuals and nymphs. Simply put, perversion, prostitution, and decadence permeated the atmosphere of the region.

4. Humanism

The region boasted the site of a magnificent, ornate, white-marble temple. It was built by Herod the Great to honor the Caesar, whom the people had deified and worshiped as a human god. It was dedicated to the "godhead of the Caesars." No doubt this grand temple was seen by Jesus and the disciples.

5. Rebellion

Believe it or not, the region of Caesarea Philippi was to become home to the legendary fortress of Nimrod. Remember Nimrod from Genesis 10:8-10 and 11:4? He was the mighty hunter who built the city and became the king of Babel. He was the rebel who inspired false worship and made a name for himself by building a tower into the heavens.

From AD 1126 to 1129, Nimrod's fortress was home to scores of Islamic radical assassins who trafficked in drugs, murdered innocent people, and lived off the countryside, robbing and raping. Today, a tourist can hike up a trail to Nimrod's lair.

Christ's very presence in the region of Caesarea Philippi was a face-off with these five symbols of evil.

Picture Jesus standing with a ragtag team of disciples, sharply silhouetted against the devil's stronghold. Satan, principalities and powers listened as Jesus stood on the rock of messianic confession and revelation to announce: "I will build my church; and the gates of hell shall not prevail against it" (Matt. 16:18 KJV).

Changing the Meaning of Church

The context in which Jesus used the word *church* forever raised the bar on its meaning. Before Matthew 16:18, *church* (Greek, *ekklesia*) had been commonly designated an assembly or gathering called together for a meeting. After Jesus' momentous declaration at Caesarea Philippi, it would forever mean "the called-out ones from the world system into discipleship, fellowship, and partnership with Christ."

> From that time Jesus began to show to His disciples that He must go to Jerusalem, and suffer many things from the elders and chief priests and scribes, and be killed, and be raised the third day (v. 21).

Six swift days after Christ's unveiling of the Church, He "was transfigured before them" on the slopes of 9,232-foot Mount Hermon, Israel's highest peak (Matt. 17:2). Jesus' face shone like the sun, and His clothes became as white as light. Peter, James, and John were transfixed and Jesus was transfigured with Moses and Elijah. He talked with them about His coming death.

Jesus announced His church under the shadow of hell's gates. But atop Mount Hermon, He was affirmed in the presence of heaven. The voice of the Father declared, "This is My beloved Son, in whom I am well pleased. Hear Him!" (v. 5).

Hear Him! *"I will build My church and the gates of hell shall not prevail against it."*

In the Greek, Jesus' announcement is not a depiction of the Church defensively protecting itself from hell's attacks. It is rather a picture of hell's gates unable to thwart the advancing Church.

But the question we face is, Why are so many churches closing? Why are so many believers absent without leave? Perhaps we need to review the biblical pictures of the Church.

The Universal Church

I read somewhere that there are 22,000 Christian denominations on planet Earth. The statistician went on to ask, "Aren't you glad you are a member of the right one?" This rhetorical question indicates that the church of the Lord Jesus Christ is larger than any single denomination. This is what the Scriptures say:

> "Take heed to yourselves and to all the flock, among which the Holy Spirit has made you overseers, to shepherd the church of God which He purchased with His own blood" (Acts 20:28).

> I am the least of the apostles...not worthy to be called an apostle, because I persecuted the church of God (1 Cor. 15:9).

> You have heard of my former conduct in Judaism, how I persecuted the church of God beyond measure and tried to destroy it (Gal. 1:13).

> Christ is head of the church; and He is the Savior of the body.... Husbands, love your wives, just as Christ also loved the church and gave Himself for her, that He might sanctify and cleanse her with the

washing of water by the word, that He might present her to Himself a glorious church, not having spot or wrinkle or any such thing, but that she should be holy and without blemish (Eph. 5:23, 25-27).

But you have come to Mount Zion and to the city of the living God, the heavenly Jerusalem . . . to the general assembly and church of the firstborn who are registered in heaven, to God the Judge of all, to spirits of the just men made perfect, to Jesus the Mediator of the new covenant, and to the blood of sprinkling that speaks better things than that of Abel (Heb. 12:22-24).

I heard, as it were, the voice of a great multitude, as the sound of many waters and as the sound of mighty thunderings, saying "Alleluia! For the Lord God Omnipotent reigns! Let us be glad and rejoice and give Him glory, for the marriage of the Lamb has come, and His wife has made herself ready (Rev. 19:6-7).

In a word, every born-again believer is a member of the universal church of Jesus Christ.

THE LOCAL CHURCH

The universal, mystical church, while very real, finds its earthly, physical expression in the local church. There are at least 105 references to the *ekklesia* in Scripture. About 95 percent of them refer to the local church. Why the many local-church references? The local church is the touch-point of cosmic conflict and earthly challenge. The local church intersects time and eternity. The apostle Paul illustrated this truth.

- Before his conversion, Paul's driving passion was to stamp out local churches (see Acts 8:3).

- After his conversion, he was committed to planting and nurturing local churches (see 14:23).

- One of Paul's heaviest burdens was the care of local churches (see 2 Cor. 11:28).

- Nine of his thirteen New Testament epistles were written to local churches.

- Three of Paul's New Testament letters were written to local-church pastors.

Paul believed the gates of hell would never prevail against Christ's universal church. He also knew the local church was the arena where the war would rage.

> For I know this, that after my departure savage wolves will come in among you, not sparing the flock. Also from among yourselves men will rise up, speaking perverse things, to draw away the disciples after themselves. Therefore watch, and remember that for three years I did not cease to warn everyone night and day with tears (Acts 20:29-31).

Paul delivered this message to the Ephesians. Just a short generation later, the Holy Spirit diagnosed the church with having left its first love. It was struggling, with death rattles in its throat (Rev. 2:4-5). Knowing the church would be threatened and even at times feel helpless, Paul gave a *prognosis* of triumph:

> I commend you to God and to the word of His grace, which is able to build you up and give you an inheritance among all those who are sanctified (Acts 20:32).

The Individual Church

The substitutionary death of Jesus Christ has redeemed billions of fallen people—one at a time. We are told that 2.2 billion Christians are alive today. Only God knows the correct number. Whatever it is, every miracle of a changed life was individual. This is the message of Ephesians 5:30: "We are members of His body, of His flesh and of His bones."

This is the meaning of 1 Corinthians 12:18-20:

> But now God has set the members, each one of them, in the body just as He pleased. And if they were all one member, where would the body be? But now indeed there are many members, yet one body.

By the Holy Spirit, Paul summarized this teaching in verse 27: "Now you are the body of Christ, and *members individually*." The Scriptures are plain:

- The church is *universal*—mystical and invisible.
- The church is *local*—vulnerable and tangible.
- The church is *individual*—touchable and personal.
- The church is *universal* but not abstract; *local* but not limited, *individual* but not isolated!

The Church is me. Where I go, the Church goes. What I do, the Church does. The way I think, the Church thinks. The Church is you—every one of you, redeemed and planted in a local assembly. The Church is us—all of us, from the thief on the cross to the last benighted sinner who will ever believe and receive. This is almost too much to comprehend! You and I share divine DNA:

> His divine power has given to us all things that pertain to life and godliness... that through these [precious promises] you may be partakers of the divine nature (2 Peter 1:3-4).

God the Father has blessed us with every spiritual blessing (Eph. 1:3). Chosen in Christ before the foundation of the world, we are accepted in the Beloved (vv. 4-6).

God the Son paid the price for our redemption through His blood and by His grace (v. 7).

God the Holy Spirit of Promise, has sealed us with a down payment on our future inheritance (vv. 13-14). Welcome to the "dispensation of the grace of God" (3:2).

> From the beginning of the ages [the Church] has been [a mystery] hidden in God who created all things through Jesus Christ; to the intent that now the manifold wisdom of God might be made known by the church to the principalities and powers in the heavenly places (vv. 9-10).

The momentous declaration that "the gates of hell shall not prevail" against the Church was made from the gates of hell itself! What Jesus proclaimed there assures us of the greatness of the Church. It assures us that the Church will not only endure—it will triumph.

Caesarea Philippi reminds us that the Church is destined for greatness. Christ has built the potential for greatness into every church; He wants no church left behind. In the next few chapters we will learn lessons from one of the truly great churches in history. Let's look at what made the church at Antioch a G.R.E.A.T. church.

Travel with me back in time. It is twenty years after the ascension of Christ, and we're going to the city of Antioch. It's located about 300 miles north and slightly west of Jerusalem. Situated on the west bank of the Orontes River, 16 miles from the Mediterranean Sea, Antioch is the capital of the rich and powerful Roman province of Syria.

At this point in history it is the third-largest city in the known world, smaller only than Rome and Alexandria. We walk through the labyrinth of streets and observe the surroundings. The city is multicultural, libertarian, wealthy, and sex-crazed. Roman soldiers are everywhere.

Although Jews live here, you can tell this is a Hellenistic city, soaked in Greek culture. Read the inscriptions on the buildings: "Lord Luck," "Lord Fate," "Lord Serapis," and "Lord Immortality."

Signs of horoscopes, magic, and astrology are everywhere. We are constantly confronted with signs of the dissolution of society. We meet a Christian citizen of Antioch and ask him to give us a guided tour and tell us about the church and its influence here. He begins:

> Yes, there is a church here. It's called the Church at Antioch, and it was planted by laymen. They came here largely as a result of persecution.
>
> Our pastor? They sent a guy named Barnabas. He recruited a fellow named Paul to be his assistant. The two were here for quite some time; and while this became their home church, they are not here now. The church has sent them out to preach and to plant

new churches, although they drop in from time to time. They looked pretty beat-up the last time they were in town.

Yes, there are Jews here, but the Jewish population isn't large. Most of the people in this church are non-Jewish. They are what you would call "Gentiles." Speaking of what people are called, this is the first place that people who follow Christ were called "Christians."

Was there communication between this church and Jerusalem? Yes, a while back the church got a special-delivery letter from the Jerusalem elders who had called a big meeting. So the Antioch church sent a delegation to the Jerusalem Council. The written report from the Council decreed that circumcision is not required of the followers of Jesus.

Do we have a real church? Absolutely. The church here in Antioch is accountable to the leaders, but we have no building where everyone gets together on Sunday. We do ministry in the workplace and in people's homes.

The people talk a lot about grace, Jesus, the Holy Spirit, and how much they love one another. These folks aren't quitters, and we have a lot of Scripture study and prayer.

By every definition, the church at Antioch was a great church. Acts 11 doesn't tell the whole story, but it gives us a cameo of what a GREAT church looks like. We can describe its greatness with the acrostic G.R.E.A.T.

Grace Church: "When [Barnabas] came [to Antioch] and [saw] the grace of God, he was glad" (v. 23).

Relationship Church: "So it was that for a whole year they assembled with the church and taught a great many people. And the disciples were first called Christians in Antioch" (v. 26).

Evangelistic Church: "And a great many people were added to the Lord" (v. 24).

Anointed Church: Barnabas was "full of the Holy Spirit" (v. 24). Agabus "showed by the Spirit" (v. 28). "The Holy Spirit said . . . " (13:2). Paul and Barnabas were "sent out by the Holy Spirit" (v. 4).

Tenacious Church: "that with purpose of heart they should continue with the Lord" (11:23).

The following chapters discuss these five elements of a G.R.E.A.T. church.

Meditating on the Message

1. Jesus announced the building of the church in Caesarea Phillipi (Matt. 16:13-19). Relate the characteristics of the region that made it "enemy territory" to conditions surrounding the local church today.

2. Discuss how the church is universal, local, and individual.

3. The five words/characteristics that complete the acrostic G.R.E.A.T. are grace, relationship, evangelistic, anointed and tenacious. How do these characteristics blend in your church?

Assignment: On a scale of 1 to 10 (with 10 being highest), rate these characteristics in your church. What can you do to make the weaker traits more dominant?

Chapter 2

A Great Church Is a Grace Church

How poignantly the Holy Spirit captured the essence of Barnabas' first visit to Antioch: "When [Barnabas] came [to Antioch] and had seen the grace of God, he was glad" (Acts 11:23).

Having heard about the happenings in Antioch, the Jerusalem church sent Barnabas on a fact-finding mission. On his first trip, Barnabas saw the grace of God. Sweet grace. Pure grace. Free grace. Personal and corporate grace. Amazing grace. God's grace!

Barnabas was an FTA at Antioch—a first-time attender. Barnabas was an observer, stranger, outsider from a different culture. His first impression was classic: *He saw the grace of God and was glad!*

What a church! This was the real deal. What do first-time attenders see when they visit your church?

Ken Houts, a friend who is the founder and president of Care Ministries International, has spent a quarter of a century researching and developing ministries designed to impact first-time attenders. His goal is to transform visitors into faithful disciples committed to the local church. He calls them "miracles waiting to happen."

Here's what Ken's research and experience have revealed about FTAs (first-time attenders):

- FTAs represent the most available, touchable, reachable harvest for any church.

- FTAs are the church of the future. No one commits to a church before he visits.

- The average American congregation loses 10 to 15 percent of its membership yearly through attrition. A church must continually reach new people just to hold its own.

- FTAs decide in the first eleven minutes if they will return to a church.

- The annual number of FTAs is about the same number as the average Sunday morning attendance.

- Statistically, only one of ten FTAs visits a second time. This means that nine out of ten FTAs will not return a second time.

- More than 75 percent of all FTAs have been personally invited by a relative or friend.

- The average believer has twenty relationships with unchurched people.

- This means the influence circle of a church is twenty times larger than the membership. A church of 100, then, has an immediate circle of influence with 2,000 unchurched people!

- More than 25 percent of Americans say they would attend a church at least once, if personally invited by a regular attender.

- At least 75 percent of all FTAs want relationships.

- One-hundred percent of FTAs have needs.

- Most churches will retain 50 percent of second-time guests for at least four to six weeks.

- Repeat guests need four friends their first month.

- FTA follow-up is 83 percent more effective if done by laypersons. FTAs expect pastor/staff follow-up, but they are impacted by laypersons who want to be their friends.[1]

What is grace? *Grace* is the multidimensional, undeserved gift of our merciful God. Grace . . .

- brings salvation (Titus 2:11)

- provides security (1 Cor. 15:10)

- perfects weakness (2 Cor. 12:9)

- seasons speech (Col. 4:5-6)

- empowers against strange doctrines (Heb. 13:9)

- enables us to submit to God (James 4:6-7).

Charis, the Greek word for grace, is used 156 times in the New Testament. It is translated "grace" 130 of those times. Paul spoke of grace 110 times, including the beginning and ending of every one of his thirteen epistles. The last chapter of the New Testament leaves us with this benediction of grace: "The grace of our Lord Jesus Christ be with you all. Amen" (Rev. 22:21).

Human attempts to describe the profundity of grace leave us feeling sorely inadequate:

> Grace is free . . . but not cheap.
>
> Grace is a gift . . . but cannot be earned.
>
> Grace must be received . . . never presumed.
>
> Grace is undeserved favor . . . never divine debt.
>
> Grace is whatever you need . . . when you need it.
>
> Grace is love . . . with no strings attached.
>
> Grace is when you get . . . what you don't deserve.
>
> Grace is power and ability . . . to do the will of God.

Antioch was a great church because it was a grace church. But how do we recognize grace? What are its distinctives? Here are some of the biblical characteristics of the grace of God.

THE SPIRIT OF GRACE—TRUE SPIRITUALITY

The Holy Spirit is called "the Spirit of grace" in Hebrews 10:29. Only those born of the Holy Spirit of grace can discover true spirituality (John 3:5). You are probably familiar with the passage "Not by might nor by power, but by My Spirit" (Zechariah 4:6). But did you know it is tied to grace?

After being captive for seventy years in Babylon, the Jews returned to Jerusalem with Zerubbabel. Within seven months, the people began work to replace Solomon's temple, which had been destroyed by Nebuchadnezzar. They were building a new place of worship.

Difficulties and distractions arose, and the project came to a halt with nothing but the foundation completed. For sixteen years, no work was done on it. For sixteen years, the site represented the incompetence of Zerubbabel and the failures of the people. Along came Zechariah with a vision from God and a divine message:

> This is the word of the Lord to Zerubbabel: "Not by might nor by power, but by My Spirit," says the Lord of hosts. "Who are you, O great mountain? Before Zerubbabel you shall become a plain! And he shall bring forth the capstone with shouts of 'Grace, grace to it!'" (Zech. 4:6-7).

In *The Message*, Eugene Peterson sheds light on the meaning of these verses in everyday language:

> This is God's message to Zerubbabel: "You can't force these things. They only come about through my Spirit," says God-of-the-Angel-Armies. "So, big mountain, who do you think you are? Next to Zerubbabel you're nothing but a molehill. He'll proceed to set the Cornerstone in place, accompanied by cheers: Yes! Yes! Do it!" (MSG).

The cheers? *"Grace, grace to it!"* In contemporary vernacular, a paraphrase of this passage of Scripture might sound like this:

Zerubbabel, the mountain that overshadows you is a sixteen-year-old, unfinished project. But I am going to send My Spirit of grace. It will enable you to do My will and accomplish My work. My Spirit, not human might or political power, will motivate you and the people. When you finish the work, you will give it the finishing touch with shouts of "Grace, grace to it!"

What a picture . . . the Holy Spirit providing grace to accomplish the work of God! The Holy Spirit did not lay one stone or hang a single door, but He gave what only He can give: grace to do God's work. Building a great church of God's people requires sweat, sacrifice, skill . . . *and the Spirit of grace!* This is what Barnabas witnessed at Antioch.

THE ATTITUDE OF GRACE— HUMILITY

Paul reminds everyone, through the grace given him, "not to think of himself more highly than he ought to think" (Rom. 12:3). James tells us to clothe ourselves with humility, and reminds us that God "resists the proud, but gives grace to the humble" (James 4:6). Humility is a prerequisite to grace, because the proud cannot accept grace. Samuel Brengle, noted Salvation Army official, was once introduced as "the great Dr. Brengle." Later, he wrote in his diary:

> The axe cannot boast of the trees it has cut down. It could do nothing but for the woodsman. He made it, he sharpened it, and he used it. The moment he throws it aside, it becomes only old iron. Oh that I may never lose sight of this.[2]

Beware, however, for humility has an enemy. It is subtle, clever and quiet. This enemy is pride—deceptive and destructive pride. Pride manifests itself in our work, our homes, cars, status, money, education, power, and sometimes our church.

Pride colors our approach to others. It secretly and subtly criticizes, condemns, condescends, classes, and complains. Once pride contaminates a person or a church, grace struggles to germinate.

J. Oswald Sanders, in his classic work *Spiritual Leadership*, writes:

> Pride takes many forms, but spiritual pride is the most grievous. To become proud of spiritual gifts or leadership position is to forget that all we have is from God, all the position we occupy is by God's appointment. The victim of pride is often least aware of the sin. Three tests help us identify the problem:
>
> *The test of precedence.* How do we react when another is selected for the position we expected to have or wanted to fill? When another is promoted in our place? When another's gifts seem greater than our own?
>
> *The test of sincerity.* In our moments of honest self-reflection, we often admit to problems and weaknesses. How do we feel when others identify the same problems in us?
>
> *The test of criticism.* Does criticism lead to immediate resentment and self-justification? Do we rush to criticize the critic? If we are honest, when we measure ourselves by the life of Jesus, who humbled Himself on the cross, we are overwhelmed with the shabbiness, the vileness, of our hearts, and we cry:

Boasting excluded, pride I abase;

I'm only a sinner, saved by grace.[3]

Reject the "either-or" trap. Some mistakenly assume that a desire to build a great church is rooted in pride. The issue is not humble mediocrity or prideful greatness. Humility is far from a weak worm groveling in the dust; it is a champion striving to expand the kingdom of God.

The humble person learns, grows, obeys, relates, serves and persists. At the same time, humility understands and embraces the fact that every advance and success is rooted firmly in the soil of God's nurturing grace. This is what Barnabas saw at Antioch.

The Heart of Grace— Integrity

The great apostle Paul makes a case for integrity in 2 Corinthians 1:12:

> For our boasting is this: the testimony of our conscience that we conducted ourselves in the world in simplicity and godly sincerity, not with fleshly wisdom but by the grace of God, and more abundantly toward you.

Later, in 2 Corinthians 2:17, Paul said, "Unlike so many, we do not peddle the word of God for profit" (NIV). He is testifying to the fact that people who live by the grace of God will have a clear conscience and approach others without hidden agendas. This is the very heart of gracious integrity.

As I write these words, I have on my desk the results of studies compiled by The American Management Association,

Santa Clara University, *Psychology Today*, Korn/Ferry International, and Columbia Graduate School of Business. The studies show the qualities most desired, looked for, and needed in corporate leadership. These are honesty, responsibility, morality, conviction, trustworthiness, and so forth. Simply put, the business world wants integrity!

How much more should *the Church* lead with integrity! The wise man said, "The integrity of the upright will guide them, but the perversity of the unfaithful will destroy them" (Prov. 11:3). Character flaws, left unchecked, always rise up to bite the hand that feeds them.

Ours is a world where courage is replaced by savvy, honesty is clouded by situation ethics, truth is cheated by expediency, absolutes are defined by relativism, and facts are given facelifts by spin doctors. Where is the integrity?

The one place people must turn to find integrity is the Church. Jesus named His followers "the salt of the earth" (Matt. 5:13). Salt is not what we do, it is what we are—the preserving, decay-defying influence of grace. The twenty-first-century church earns the right to be heard only by its moral authority. Jesus announced, "I have come into the world, that I should bear witness to the truth" (John 18:37). Dare we do less?

What do we model for the next generation? Ruth Baron is right: "We set young leaders up for a fall if we encourage them to envision what they can do before they consider the kind of person they should be." Our integrity quotient is more important than our intelligence quotient.

Integrity Quotient Test

1. Do I deal in duplicity, insincerity, mask-wearing, and hidden agendas?

2. Do I try to cleverly outsmart others by spinning the truth to my advantage?

3. Do I justify questionable actions and attitudes in myself by trying to make the end justify the means?

4. Do I require accountability in others, while excusing it in myself?

5. Do I keep my commitments, even if doing so requires sacrifice on my part?

6. Do I stand up for what is right, even if it means standing alone?

7. When I fail, do I ask forgiveness from God or others, learn from my mistakes, and clean up my mess?

8. Do I lose confidence in others for the same things I rationalize as okay for myself?

9. If asked, would my family say I am a person of integrity?

10. Can I improve?

Still as of old
Men by themselves are priced—
For thirty pieces Judas sold
Himself, not Christ.
—"Judas," by Hester H. Cholmondeley

THE FACE OF GRACE—
INDIVIDUALITY

Take out your driver's license. Look at the picture. What do you see? I know. It's your bad side and it looks like a mug shot! But really, what do you see? Right—yourself! Your face reflects your individuality. People recognize you by your face. Your face expresses what people know as your uniqueness. You are what you are.

Paul would agree. Speaking of himself as an apostle, Paul said, "By the grace of God I am what I am" (1 Cor. 15:10). Like all of us, Paul had a bad side—he had "persecuted the church of God" (v. 9); and a good side—he had seen the Lord (v. 8). Paul's countenance reflected grace—different, unique, and individual.

I heard Pastor Rick Warren talk about a believer's "shape." He says we're all different in five important ways:

S—Spiritual gifts. All of us have one or more spiritual gifts that help us understand what we are to do in the church.

H—Heart. Within each heart is the revelation of what we love to do.

A—Abilities. Everyone has certain God-given, natural talents and skills.

P—Personality. Our disposition helps to define where we are best fitted to serve.

E—Experiences. Spiritual, educational, ministry, and even painful experiences are direct influences on us.

Wrap this up with the ribbon of grace and there you have it: I am what I am! Churches and leaders who recognize the face of grace are able to help believers reach maximum potential for meaningful, God-glorifying living.

This message isn't just for leaders, it is for followers. Don't just volunteer to help and then sit idly by, waiting for an already overworked leader to hold your hand. Display some initiative.

1. Know who you are. You are unique. God does not make us with a cookie cutter. Refuse to compare your weaknesses with others' strengths. Resist the urge to compare your lack of gifts with others' giftedness. Reject the notion that another person's achievements are more valuable than yours.

Gordon Michow once wrote:

> All of my life I have tried to please others. All of my life I have tried to be like others. I will not do this. If I take all of my time to be like someone else, who will take the time to be me?

Ethel Barrett said, "We wouldn't worry much about what others think of us if we knew how seldom they did."

2. Show who you are. Invest yourself in discovering your spiritual gifts. Pray for the Holy Spirit to reveal the passion of your heart. Take inventory of your abilities. Learn more about your personality characteristics with a personality test. Reflect on the past to determine the experiences profoundly influencing your life. Now, put your individuality to work making a difference. You don't have to *be the best*, but you must *do your best*. Grace makes it happen!

3. *Grow where you are.* Make personal growth a priority. Be willing to experiment with a variety of ministry opportunities until you find what you fit best. Take your time to grow deep. It is not how fast or how far you plow, it is how deep! If you take care of the depth, God will take care of the breadth. Barnabas definitely saw the face of grace at Antioch!

THE HAND OF GRACE—
GENEROSITY

Antioch was a generous church. Hearing from the Holy Spirit "there was going to be a great famine throughout all the world," the disciples "determined to send relief to the brethren dwelling in Judea.... They... sent it to the elders by the hands of Barnabas and Saul" (Acts 11:28-30).

The prophecy of a coming famine in the whole world meant the economy of Antioch itself was about to take a hit. Though famine was imminent, Antioch showed generous grace by sending a relief offering. *The procedure* was for the offering to be hand-delivered by Barnabas and Saul. Paul learned something at Antioch he later wrote about in 2 Corinthians 8 and 9: *The hand of grace is generosity!* Paul mentions *grace* seven times in chapter 8 and three times in chapter 9. The bottom line: Grace and giving are twins!

> But as you abound in everything—in faith, in speech, in knowledge, in all diligence, and in your love for us—see that you abound in this grace also (8:7).

A church can believe, speak, know, work, and love, but without giving, it fails to fully express God's grace. In the Old Testament, God said, "If you will do this and that, I will bless you." In the New Testament, He says, "You are already blessed, so reflect My grace."

We give to express and release God's grace. The New Testament church becomes God's hand extended—generously dispensing God's grace. Not every local church has learned this grace truth.

There are basically two kinds of churches: the *gravity church* and the *grace church*. The *gravity church* gives in response to the pull of earth. Conversely, the *grace church* gives in response to the pull of heaven.

Here's how a person in a *gravity church* is influenced by the pull of earth:

- *Fearfully.* "If I don't give, God will punish me."
- *Tearfully.* "It breaks my heart to give away my hard-earned money."
- *Near-fully.* "I don't mind giving to help locally, but don't ask me to give outside of my church."
- *Peer-fully.* "I sure hope my peers find out how much I give."
- *Year-fully.* "I need to increase my giving this year because I need the income-tax deduction."

A person giving in a *grace church* is influenced by the pull of heaven:

- *Sacrificially* (2 Cor. 8:2). "I'll give something of value in exchange for something of greater value."
- *Willingly* (v. 3). "No one manipulates or forces me to give. My will is in agreement with God's will."
- *Worshipfully* (v. 5). "My giving is first and foremost an offering of worship to God, regardless of where it will be directed."
- *Cheerfully* (9:7). "Hallelujah! I have another opportunity to express the grace of God!"
- *Liberally* (v. 8). "I do not give to get. But when I give, I get, and that enables me to give again. Like grace, there is no end."

THE BEHAVIOR OF GRACE—RESPONSIBILITY

What Barnabas saw in the believers at Antioch was that grace transformed their behavior. Let me illustrate. Take a coin. Flip it in the air. Call it . . . heads or tails? Like a coin, grace has two sides: the *resource* side and the *responsibility* side.

Grace is a free gift but not a free ride. It impacts our behavior. Dallas Willard said:

> Grace is opposed to earning righteousness (or works), but grace is not opposed to effort. You can't will or work your way into the kingdom, but living in contact with God does take effort. I think it was Augustine who cut a path between unaided human initiative and total passivity when he said, "Without God, we cannot; without us God will not."[4]

The aposte Paul said it like this:

> For the grace of God that brings salvation has appeared to all men, teaching us that, denying ungodliness and worldly lusts, we should live soberly, righteously, and godly in the present age, looking for the blessed hope and glorious appearing of our great God and Savior Jesus Christ, who gave Himself for us, that He might redeem us from every lawless deed and purify for Himself His own special people, zealous for good works. Speak these things, exhort, and rebuke with all authority. Let no one despise you (Titus 2:11-15).

Like some today, the people to whom Titus was ministering assumed that because grace was free, it was also cheap. Lutheran pastor Dietrich Bonhoeffer, who was martyred by the Nazis at the young age of thirty-nine, called this one-sided grace "cheap grace." He wrote:

> Cheap grace is the deadly enemy of our Church. We are fighting today for costly grace. Cheap grace means sold on the market like cheapjacks' wares. The sacraments, the forgiveness of sin, and the consolations of religion are thrown away at cut prices. . . . The essence of grace, we suppose, is that the account has been paid in advance; and, because it has been paid, everything can be had for nothing. . . . In such a church the world finds a cheap covering for its sins; no contrition is required, still less any real desire to be delivered from sin. . . . Cheap grace is the grace we bestow on ourselves.

Cheap grace is the preaching of forgiveness without requiring repentance, baptism without church discipline, Communion without confession, absolution without personal confession. Cheap grace is grace without discipleship, grace without the cross, grace without Jesus Christ, living and incarnate.[5]

Remember those two sides of the coin of grace—*resource* and *responsibility*? God's grace is our inexplicable resource, but it is also our solemn and sacred responsibility. Look at the contrast:

The Resource of Grace	Our Response
Freely given (Acts 11:23)	May be rendered ineffective (2 Cor. 6:1)
Anoints for service (1 Cor. 3:10)	Not given for selfishness (1 Peter 4:10)
Provides a simple lifestyle (2 Cor. 1:12)	Rejects bondages (Gal. 5:1)
Sufficient for all needs (2 Cor. 12:9)	Must be wisely appropriated (1 Peter 4:10)
Bestowed on sinners (1 Tim. 1:12)	Never excuses sin (Rom. 6:15)
Opens the door of salvation (Acts 15:11)	Closes the door on sin (Rom. 6:1)
Prepares for justification (Rom. 5:1-2)	Requires dying to sin (Rom. 6:6)
Abounds to all (Rom. 5:15)	Can be missed (Heb. 12:15)

Not dependent on good works (Rom. 11:6)	Followed by good works (Titus 3:7-14)
Has appeared to all (Titus 2:11)	Can be perverted (Jude 4)
Destroys legalism (Gal. 2:21)	Teaches to deny ungodliness (Titus 2:12)
Means for effectiveness (Eph. 3:7-8)	Can be set aside (Gal. 2:21)
Promotes fruitfulness (Col. 1:16)	Demonstrated in sacrifice (2 Cor. 8:9)

The grace revelation is to see grace as a total life experience. Grace is for the sinner, but thank God it is also for the saint. Dallas Willard says, "A sinner needs grace, but a saint goes through it like a jet goes through jet fuel."[6] Thus, Paul could say:

> But by the grace of God I am what I am, and His grace toward me was not in vain; but I labored more abundantly than they all, yet not I, but the grace of God which was with me (1 Cor. 15:10).

Some time ago I was facing a difficult assignment—one I dreaded, to say the least. I slipped into bed, unable to quiet my anxiety. Lying there open-eyed, staring at the darkness, I said to my wife, Peggy, "Boy, I dread this weekend. The Lord is going to have to give me extra grace to get through it." She answered, "He already has."

That's it! Whatever responsibilities confront us, grace is ours. *He has already provided!* No wonder great churches are grace churches. They are resourced abundantly and they behave responsibly.

A Gallery of Grace

Grace happens when we get what we don't deserve. A great church is always a grace church. The world has enough grief and guilt. Let's give grace!

Late one Saturday night in 1987, a young pastor prayed, "Lord, we will love anyone You send to us." Ten hours later two homosexuals showed up in church, dressed in black leather and wearing earrings. They walked to the front and sat in the first row, near the center aisle.

Oh no! the pastor thought, *I pray they are not here to cause trouble.* Just then the Lord reminded him of the prayer he had prayed hours earlier. When the invitation was given, the two men were first to the altar.

Their story unfolded. The night before—about the same time the pastor was praying his "we'll-love-anyone" prayer—the older of the two was on the verge of suicide. He had spent twenty years in the gay lifestyle. He had abused drugs, alcohol, and sex. He had wasted his youth and grieved his family.

In the stinking restroom of a gay bar, facing himself in a dingy mirror, he wept and prayed, "God, I don't know if You're there; but if You are, please help me."

Both men were miraculously saved that Sunday. A singles group took them under its wing, loved them, led them, and discipled them. The younger one moved on with his life; and at last report, was still following Jesus.

The older guy, Wayne Andre, matured in his faith and married a beautiful lady from the church. They adopted two lovely little girls. He wrote his autobiography, and founded and directs a ministry to the sexually broken, called *Free My Children*.

Wayne has ministered to hundreds and discipled scores of men and women. He provides ongoing care and evangelism to dying AIDS patients. Today, twenty years later, he is one of the most respected leaders in his church. I know the story is true—I saw the miracle unfold! I was the pastor. What is just as important is that God used Wayne to teach me some life-changing lessons.

If you think this story is only about homosexuals needing grace, you missed it! Whether your life's résumé was littered with sexual immorality or dirtied by self-righteousness, you were still dead in trespasses and sin. Sin once abounded in your life; grace now abounds even more!

Remember this the next time you are tempted to look down your nose at lost, broken, troubled, rejected, abused people. They have enough guilt and grief. They need what you've got—amazing grace!

No wonder the first thing Barnabas saw at Antioch was the grace of God. And no wonder he was glad. Grace is the first mark of greatness!

MEDITATING ON THE MESSAGE

1. How does pride impact outreach evangelism? List the three tests by which we can measure our struggle with pride.

2. A *gravity church* and a *G.R.A.C.E. church* differ in perspective and motivations. How do these concepts relate to the perspective and motivation of your church?

3. Discuss *responsibility* and the health of the local church.

Assignment: At the next church service, pretend you are a first-time attender—FTA. Write down what you think a guest's first impressions would be.

Chapter 3

A GREAT CHURCH IS A RELATIONSHIP CHURCH

Relationships are a necessary and integral part of the Church. We have learned that a great church is a G.R.E.A.T. church. While **G** represents *grace*, the second letter, **R**, signals *relationship*. Christianity is not a religion. It is a faith-based relationship.

- It was relationship that God desired with Adam and Eve (Gen. 3:8-9).

- God wanted relationship with Israel (Deut. 7:6-9).

- The Ten Commandments are purely relational: the first four are with God, the remaining six with people (Ex. 20:3-17).

- Jesus' Sermon on the Mount was a sermon about relationships (Matt. 5-7).

- Christ and the Church are in relationship. The Church is the body; Christ is the head. The Church is God's building; Christ is the chief cornerstone. The Church is God's flock; Christ is the Good Shepherd. The Church is God's temple; Christ is the High Priest. The Church is the bride; Christ is the Bridegroom. The Church is the branches; Christ is the Vine.

- Believers are in relationship with other believers (1 Cor. 12:26-27).

THE G.R.E.A.T. CHURCH IN THE BIBLE

Let's look again at our great church example, the first church of Antioch. It exemplifies the unique ways a church relates.

First, the church at Antioch had relationship with God. The same God who permitted the persecution and scattering of the Jewish church in Jerusalem initiated an ingathering of Gentiles in Antioch (Acts 11:19-20).

Second, the church at Antioch had a relationship with Jesus. After hearing the message of Jesus, "a great number believed and turned to the Lord" (v. 21).

Third, the church at Antioch had a relationship with the Holy Spirit. The believers embraced Barnabas, who was "full of the Holy Spirit" (v. 24). They responded to Agabus, "[who] stood up and showed by the Spirit that there was going to be a great famine" (v. 28). It was the Holy Spirit who said, "Now separate to Me Barnabas and Saul for the work to which I have called them" (13:2).

Fourth, the Antioch believers had a relationship with one another. Relationships were actually better in Antioch than in Jerusalem. At Jerusalem, Jewish believers looked down their noses on Gentiles, if they looked at them at all. But in Antioch, for the first time in both principle and habit, Jews and Gentiles ate, prayed, worshiped, studied, and worked together!

What's more, the names of the leaders at Antioch boldly underscore their relationship with one another. They are listed in 13:1:

> Barnabas—a Cypriot landowner and Levite
>
> Simeon—clearly a black man who was nicknamed "Niger," or "the swarthy"
>
> Lucius—from Cyrene in North Africa, probably a man of color
>
> Manaen—a close friend of Herod's family, very much an aristocrat
>
> Saul—a fiery young intellectual from Tarsus and former Jewish Pharisee

Relationships? This multicultural group fasted and prayed *together* (v. 3)!

Fifth, believers at Antioch had a relationship with non-believers. "And the disciples were first called Christians in Antioch" (11:26). Who coined this word *Christian?* Certainly not the unbelieving Jews. *Christ* means "Anointed One" and "Messiah." A good Jew would never have affirmed Christ in that way.

Believers did not coin the word. They had already designated themselves as "disciples," "believers," "brethren," and "those of the Way." Most likely, it was a term of derision that evolved from unsaved Gentiles in the streets of Antioch. Believers were taking their newly discovered joy to the streets, sharing Christ with the unsaved.

Sixth, the church at Antioch had a relationship with truth. For a whole year Barnabas and Saul "assembled with the church and taught a great many people" (v. 26).

George Barna's research reveals that 66 percent of Americans do not believe in absolute truth. What do they believe? Many say relativism, others deconstructionism, still others anti-historicalism, revisionism . . . and the rest? Who knows what they believe?

RELATIONSHIP AND TRUTH

The relationship between truth and God has been on the minds of great thinkers. A relationship with truth is not about teaching alone. Truth is not really taught until it has been learned; learning hasn't really occurred until our minds and behaviors are changed (see Heb. 5:12-14).

A relationship with truth is not about knowledge alone. Knowledge alone puffs up (1 Cor. 8:1). It is not about communicating the letter of the law. "The letter kills, but the spirit gives life" (2 Cor. 3:6). A relationship with truth is not limited to a lecture. Paul "reasoned . . . from the scriptures, explaining and demonstrating" (Acts 17:2-3).

Truth is sound doctrine.

- It is truth because it is absolute.
- It is sound because it is indestructible.
- It is doctrine because it instructs us about how to live in this present age (Titus 2:1-15).

Antioch had a now-knowing, ongoing, ever-growing relationship with truth. Great churches today need the same relationship. Here are eighteen reasons why:

1. It supplies the need for an authoritative standard by which we live in confidence.
2. It provides "backbone" that gives uprightness in all things.
3. It shapes our moral, ethical, spiritual, and relational stan-dards.
4. It safeguards us from error.
5. It enables us to know what to respect and what to reject.
6. It brings order and simplicity by pulling many aspects of the Christian faith together.
7. It gives substance and sustenance to our faith.
8. It stabilizes us during times of testing.

9. It equips us to handle the scriptures accurately.

10. It lifts our confidence.

11. It filters out fears and superstitions.

12. It defends us against the subtleties of fortune, fame, pleasure, and power.

13. It reinforces balance in our lives.

14. It defines our lifestyle and directs our philosophy.

15. It enhances our worship and prompts our praise.

16. It defeats Satan and sets us free.

17. It is the forever-enduring Word of God.

18. It is personified in Jesus Christ our Lord.

WHY GOD PROGRAMS DIVERSITY INTO OUR PERSONAL RELATIONSHIPS

Why does God place all kinds of people in a church, challenging us to interact with each other as brothers and sisters? Why does God deem it so vital to have a melting pot of people with conflicting and competing personalities working together in the church? I believe there are at least five reasons.

To Learn Love

We have the "Adam" stain on us, a stain inherited from Adam and Eve as a result of the Fall. We were not born knowing how to relate to one another. Our parents, teachers, and society have tried to teach us relationship skills. We desperately need to learn love.

Love is not an emotion. It is a decision, a commitment. Love is not a feeling; it's a force. We call this kind of love *agape*, or the God kind of love. The God kind of love is unconditional. His love for us is not based on whether we deserve it or how we may treat Him. (Thank God, it isn't!) *Agape* love cannot love us any more or any less.

> The Lord your God has chosen you to be his own special treasure. The Lord did not choose you and lavish his love on you because you were larger or greater... for you were the smallest of all!... It was simply because the Lord loves you (Deut. 7:6-8 NLT).

Think of His love for you—unmeasured, unrationed, inexplicable! Can you give the same kind of love? Since it's more than a feeling or an emotion, God has placed us in relational laboratory so that through a myriad of relational experiences, we can reflect the love that has been so affectionately bestowed on us. To be a great church we must learn patience with firmness, compassion with discipline, and mercy with justice—all bound by love.

As a young pastor, I was challenged by this profound truth. After a few years of little growth, our church began to attract new people, win the lost, and realize growth. Many who were saved out of painful pasts lacked relational skills.

Anger, threats, cursing, and manipulation were just a few of the behaviors these baby Christians were exhibiting. I became exasperated with their on-again, off-again, conditional love. One day I said to one of the elders: "These new Christians are driving me crazy! When will they ever get it? I'm not sure

I'm even cut out for working with them when they mess up so much."

The wise man to whom I vented my frustration lectured me sternly: "Wait a minute, Pastor. You are talking about new Christians who have known little, if anything, about the love of God. They've been abused, neglected, and rejected. They've been hooked on drugs, alcohol, sex—they have never been in or around church before. Few have ever seen love modeled. Before you give up on them, you have to remember that Christianity is more than saying a prayer with them and getting them saved. They must be discipled. Discipleship is teaching people the language of love. If the church doesn't teach these people how to love, who will?"

Lovingly, but properly chastised, I changed my attitude and found my frustration level decreasing and my relationship with people intensifying in a satisfying way. Those new to the Kingdom often come from parental, sibling, and peer relationships where they have been rejected, abused, used, dominated, and manipulated. We must demonstrate a new example of relationships. We're here to learn love and give it away!

To Forge Forgiveness

Like love, forgiveness does not come naturally. It must be forged on the anvil of broken relationships. To forgive is the toughest task of all, and the least appreciated. Jesus taught us to forgive those who wrong us. He said, "If you do not forgive men . . . neither will your Father forgive your trespasses" (Matt. 6:15).

Jesus' first work on the cross was to forgive the brutish Roman soldiers who gambled for His garment. Jesus prayed, "Father, forgive them . . . they do not know what they do" (Luke 23:34). He had taught forgiveness; at the cross, in a glorious way, He was demonstrating it!

Read the passage in the Greek and you discover the words imply He "continued to say it, building to a crescendo." The words *Father, forgive them* reverberated like an echo, trumpeting Christ's compassion and putting humanity on notice that His forgiveness is complete!

Many fail to forgive because they misunderstand what forgiveness is. The idea of forgiveness is often based on false assumptions.

False assumption #1: Forgiveness is an invitation to hurt me again.

False assumption #2: Forgiveness is denial. "I forgive you; what you did to me didn't cause me any pain."

False assumption #3: Forgiveness is permission to hurt me again.

False assumption #4: Forgiveness is approval. "What you did is all right. To get your approval of me, I approve of what you did to me."

False assumption #5: Forgiveness is illogical. "To forgive is silly. It is stupid. Only a simpleton forgives."

We must learn to cancel the debt for the hurt someone gave to us. One person said, "I thought forgiveness would set my enemy free; but once I forgave, I discovered my enemy was me." To forge forgiveness, we must use the *Forgiveness Equation*.

- In *unforgiveness*, a wrong = injury = debt = payback
- In *forgiveness*, a wrong = injury = debt = cancelled debt.

To Make Muscles

God puts us in relationships—and a diversity of them—because He knows they build moral and spiritual muscles in us.

A lady who was a borderline idealist volunteered to work in our church office. After a few days of what I considered to be rather ordinary, she walked out and left me a note. It read: "This place is not a church; it's a zoo! I quit!"

Welcome to the real world. Born-again people can get on your nerves, hurt your feelings, make demands, ignore your opinions, and sometimes be downright rude! I don't know who wrote it, but I read an old Irish saying that sums it up:

> To live above with the saints we love,
>   that will be praise and glory;
>
> But to live below with the saints we know,
>   now that's another story.

Great churches with strong ministries require strong people. One reason the Lord puts us in a community of diversity called the Church is to help us build ministry muscles.

The church is not a zoo; it's a gymnasium. In the church we do resistance training to prevent weakness and flabbiness caused by atrophy. We do endurance training to enhance our ability to crash through life's quitting points. We do strength training to build us up as overcomers. We do flexibility training to prevent stiffening that comes with age.

A pastor once told me of a small town where he served that had fewer than 7,000 population. There were seven Church of God congregations inside the city limits. Six of the seven had the same mother church, but all had been birthed out of relational division.

I can't help wondering what would have been the result of the six churches, had they been birthed out of strength instead of splits. Rather than their facilities being seen by the community as memorials of immaturity, they could have been symbols of strength.

Yes, we sometimes deal with issues so principle-centered we have to agree to disagree (see Acts 15:39-40). Sometimes we have to be on the receiving end of a rebuke (see Gal. 2:11). Sometimes we are stung by the reality of rejection (see 2 Tim. 4:10). Sometimes we are victims of evil people (see v. 14). But don't waste your woes—use them to make yourself stronger! Joseph had it right: "You meant evil against me; but God meant it for good" (Gen. 50:20).

The question is not "Will we have heavy relationships?" The question is "Will we use the difficult relationships to make us stronger?" There are benefits.

1. *Grinding relationships* polish our personalities.

2. *Uncomfortable relationships* sharpen our people skills as iron sharpens iron (Prov. 27:17).

3. *Eye-opening relationships* reveal blind spots.

4. *Tedious relationships* teach us patience.

5. *Confrontational relationships* provide correction or direction.

6. *Challenging relationships* increase our influence.

7. *Encouraging relationships* energize faith.

8. *Loving relationships* build trust.

9. *Forgiving relationships* create new beginnings.

10. *Exemplary relationships* reflect Jesus. It doesn't get any stronger than this!

To Develop Disciples

Discipleship is more lived out than lectured out. Twelve sessions of discipleship studies can organize and prioritize subject matter. Only life impact, however, can transform. Discipleship is a learning relationship. John Maxwell says, "You impress from a distance; you impact up close!"

Discipleship happens when the older teach the younger, the experienced show the inexperienced, the knowledgeable inform the ignorant.

His name is Walter Wilson. He raised four beautiful daughters and a dozen spiritual sons. "Brother Wilson" is what we called him. He was my Sunday school teacher for four years.

I met him when I was age nine, in a musty basement Sunday school room. His props were creek banks, sandlots, campsites, and a '48 model Plymouth. His tools were the Bible, prayer, understanding, discipline, and gentleness. His power was truth, consistency and commitment. We moved away when I was twelve. His words, underscored by his walk, left the footprints of Jesus on my soul.

This was Jesus' model for developing disciples. He did more than teach, preach, or lecture. His primary method was making disciples through relationships with people.

Jesus always focused on relationships, whether He was . . .

Attending a wedding (John 2:1-10)

Walking along the seashore (Matt. 4:18-22)

Teaching in the synagogue (Luke 4:15)

Visiting in the home of some of the Twelve (Mark 1:29)

Eating breakfast with the disciples (2:15)

Calling on a man at his office (v. 14)

Taking a rest at a village well (John 4:1-26)

Addressing the multitudes (Matt. 4:25)

Meeting with a religious official at night (John 3:1-2)

Attending a feast in Jerusalem (5:1-8)

Teaching on the mountainside (6:1-14)

Passing through Jericho (9:1-9).

Our best way of developing disciples is through relationships.

To Embrace Eternity

Diverse relationships prepare us to embrace eternity. Life is boot camp; church is rehearsal for ruling and reigning in eternity.

What will heaven be like? We won't just float on clouds, twang harps, eat grapes, and dangle our feet in the River of Life. We will be in relationships—relationships without pain and tears.

In Ephesians 3:9-11, the apostle Paul declared that "the eternal purpose which [God] accomplished in Christ Jesus our Lord" was to make known, *through the Church*, the wisdom of God. He makes this glorious truth known to all the hosts of the spiritual realm, including "the principalities and powers."

In eternity, Jesus Christ, heaven's Bridegroom, will parade a victorious Church before all the hosts of heaven—the angels, archangels, and heavenly creatures John saw on Patmos! He will parade His bride before principalities, evil powers, and even hell itself, proclaiming in a triumphant shout of victory:

> *This is how I did it. I accomplished the eternal plan of the Father for the ages by defeating sin and Satan at the Cross, by My resurrection and through My Church—these people, the overcomers who learned how to live together in relationship!*

MEDITATING ON THE MESSAGE

1. Discuss the nature of the six relationships that defined greatness in the church at Antioch.

2. There are five reasons God programs diversity into our personal relationships. How do gifts, acceptance, and affirmation fit into diversity?

3. List some ways God has helped you to grow through diverse relationships.

Assignment: Of the ten relationships listed on page 78, which gives you the most problems? Outline positive steps of action to help you correct them.

Chapter 4

A GREAT CHURCH IS AN EVANGELISTIC CHURCH

Events surrounding the birth of the church at Antioch are revealing. Who ever heard of a program of evangelism like this?

> Men from Cyprus and Cyrene, who, when they had come to Antioch, spoke to the Hellenists, preaching the Lord Jesus (Acts 11:20).

Read the verse again—three times! Then describe in your own words what happened at Antioch. The Holy Spirit reveals three truths in this verse.

First, the news of Jesus did not get to Antioch by way of the apostles from Jerusalem. The Gospel came through unnamed, unofficial men—two or more—from Cyprus and Cyrene.

Second, men "spoke."

Third, the Greek word for *preaching* here is *euanggelizo*, meaning "to proclaim good news." Look at what this verse reveals:

- *Who?* Unnamed, unofficial men, *not* apostles, from Jerusalem.
- *What?* They proclaimed the good news at Antioch. They "spoke" to the Hellenists (the Greeks).
- *How?* They used a conversational style. The Greek word for *spoke* means "simple speech, common exchange." Today, we call it conversation.

What a surprise! Most of us thought lifestyle evangelism was invented in the twentieth century. The church at Antioch was born out of an evangelistic style based on conversational, relational interaction with unbelievers.

The main street of the city of Antioch was four miles long. Imagine the Christ-conversations that took place on that one street. Small wonder the church at Antioch eclipsed the mother church in Jerusalem to become one of the greatest churches in Christianity. It was evangelistic to the core. "And the disciples were first called Christians in Antioch" (Acts 11:26).

CHURCHES THAT FORGET SOULS DIE

Many things can affect the growth and health of the Church. The most important factor, however, is not deep preaching, benevolent action, or community involvement. A church cannot be great if it is not committed to building the population of heaven. A church can die—and God will let it—if it forgets the value of a soul.

No Church Left Behind

I interviewed Dr. Ira North when I was in my twenties and he was in his seventies. I admired him because he had led his church from 100 people to over 5,000.

"What is your advice on building the church?" I asked.

He was quiet for a few moments. Then tears filled his eyes. In a voice choking with emotion, he said: "The poorest little girl who rides to church on a bus, whose mother is a junkie and whose father has abandoned her—that little girl is worth more to Jesus than all the buildings and money this church owns. My advice if you want to build a church is: *Don't ever forget this truth!*"

Everyone who reads this book will agree that keeping the truth fresh is not easy. But how can we reach people in the strange new world of the twenty-first century? We don't need another personal soulwinning method. We have the best available, and I thank God for all of them.

The Roman Road, Four Spiritual Laws, Evangelism Explosion—all these books are wonderful. They have been used by God and believers to lead literally millions of people to a saving knowledge of Christ. We have great tools. Bill Hybels and Mark Mittelberg's *Contagious Church* series about evangelism is excellent. I have used them all and I have taught them all. What we need, however, is a good swift kick in the posterior! Would that help? Most of us know what to do and how, we just don't perform. Let me tell you the story of how a good kick helped me.

The Pastor Sets the Stage

Some years ago, the church where I was pastor employed Dr. Dan Reiland from John Maxwell's InJoy Consulting Group to consult with us about church growth. For several months Dan gathered data, studied our history, took a congregational survey, and interviewed the staff, elders, and me.

Then came the moment of truth—the diagnostic meeting with the senior pastor. I was more than a little anxious about what he would say, but I wasn't prepared for it! He used his words to give me a good, solid kick.

He said, "Raymond, you are not personally leading this church in reaching the unchurched."

What? I expected some hocus-pocus, high talk, a little impressive and fancy footwork, a few dozen compliments, some encouragement about vision and mission. How dare that audacious man take our good money and then have the gall to talk to me like he did!

He continued: "You are not personally involved in building relationships with unchurched people. You are not engaged with the culture around you. You are not intentional enough with your schedule."

"Well," I fumbled for words, "I-I-I am busy. I'm overseeing building construction. I'm developing leaders. I'm preaching four times on Sundays. I have administrative duties. I have a budget to manage. I'm in meetings. . . . "

"Listen to me," he demanded. "If you don't get engaged with your culture, intentionally build relationships with un-churched people; if *you* don't lead people to Jesus and baptize them in your baptistry, your church will plateau and decline."

He was merciless. "It has probably already plateaued," he jabbed. "You just don't know it yet!"

We paid Dan, sent him on his way, and I was glad to see him off. But, honestly, I was more mad than glad. He had forced me to face the truth! He was right. I knew it in my heart. I wasn't doing what I knew to do. The neat thing is, I didn't have to pray through over this, I just had to "get with the program."

FACING THE FACTS

I bought a health club membership and became active in a gymnasium where I got serious about building genuine relationships with unchurched people. It took years to build trustworthy relationships with some. They were suspicious of preachers. I prayed secretly for them every day and worked out "for God" in the gym about three times a week.

The Holy Spirit used me to lead about thirty unchurched people to Christ. After more than five years of building a relationship with two of the gym owners, I led them and their wives to Jesus. They were baptized and joined our church.

I'm still angry with Dan Reiland—and you can tell him if you see him! But there's more. That incident changed our church. What Dan Reiland told me turned my heart—and the heart of the church—toward the lost.

You see, this is the issue: Lost people matter to God! Can anything be worse than being lost? Dr. Gene D. Rice answers, "Yes, being lost and having no one looking for you."

THE LITANY OF THE LOST

In Luke 15, Jesus tells three compelling parables: one about a lost sheep, one about a lost coin, and one about a lost son (see vv. 7, 10, 22-24). In each of the three, a big party celebrated the occasions when the lost was found. Get the picture? Heaven doesn't rejoice when we break a record, build a building, or preach a great sermon. Heaven rejoices when the lost are found!

God did not raise up the Church to make bad people good, or good people better. He raised up the Church to make dead people live. Great churches have decided that the death of Jesus is not going to be in vain in their cities.

WE NEED EVANGELISTIC ACTION

Surfing the Internet one day, I went to *SimplyHired.com*, a search engine for jobs. I typed in the word *evangelist*, and found 951 matches. Amazingly, only one out of the first fifty was church-related. The world has adopted the title "evangelist." Microsoft and Apple Computer Companies hire a lot of them! A great church needs as much action as it does instruction when it comes to reaching the lost. These five actions are vital.

1. Get an Attitude

That's right! We can read, write, go to seminars, watch DVDs, and tinker with church structure until the cows come home. But unless we display the attitude that lost people matter, really matter to God, nothing is worth the time and effort spent on it.

Bill Hybels told of being sensitive to the Spirit's leading when it didn't make sense. One of his responsibilities at home was to take out the garbage. Every Tuesday night this pastor of a megachurch would drag the garbage cans out to the curb.

One cold January evening he didn't bother to put on shoes because he intended to hurry back up the driveway before his toes froze. As he tiptoed down the driveway as fast as he could with dignity, he noticed his new neighbor across the cul-de-sac was taking the garbage out as well.

Hybels deposited his own trash can at the curb and started to sprint up the driveway, when God spoke to him, "Go across the cul-de-sac and introduce yourself to that guy."

After arguing with God momentarily, Hybels reluctantly walked across the cul-de-sac and said, "Hi, I'm Bill Hybels, your neighbor across the street. Welcome to the neighborhood." The man told him his name and said, "I own the new car dealership down the street."

For a year, the two men met on Tuesday nights in the cul-de-sac and chatted across the garbage cans. Little by little, the man who preached to thousands every week shared Christ with one man on Tuesday evenings. Eventually, the pastor led the man and his wife to the Lord, and they are members of his church.[1] Be sensitive to the leading of the Holy Spirit. Get an attitude.

2. Engage the Culture

Unlike another "saint" from Antioch 300 years later, the early church engaged the culture. They lived in the culture but did not embrace it.

Simon Stylite lived at Antioch, Syria, in the fourth century. He was weird, but he was no sissy saint. Rather, he was bold and strong and brash! He wanted to be like God so much that he built a tall pillar with a platform atop it and began spending his days and nights up there. Taking Christ's instruction to give up all things, he felt he was "being holy," or "separating himself from the world."

This Pillar Saint, as later generations called him, received so much attention for his "noble deeds for Christ" that he kept building higher and higher towers. He spent a total of thirty-seven years on different pillars, each loftier than the previous. The last one he occupied before his death in AD 460 was sixty-six feet high. He was seventy-two when he died.

Simon Stylite accomplished what he was seeking. He attracted attention. He received accolades. He often peered over the platform and rebuked the onlookers for their sinful lives. He urged holiness of life. When he died, he was deified for his efforts and "made a saint." Thus, he is called St. Simon Stylite.

I wonder how many people would have been won to Christ had he engaged the culture rather than living above it. What if, instead of isolating himself atop a pompous pillar, he had climbed down and shared the Gospel? What if he had urged others to devote their lives to Christ instead of living like a hermit?

The twenty-first-century culture has a lot in common with first-century culture. Pluralistic, experience-driven, subjective, multilingual, and sex-soaked, both reject absolute truth and demand tolerance. In both, you must engage the culture without embracing its values.

The first-century church incarnated love, behaved godly, actualized care, and unabashedly identified with Jesus. They were not trying to win the world to an institution, but to Jesus. They did not say, "Be like us"; instead they said, "Be like Him!" They were engaged.

3. Be Intentional

Intentionality is the key. Paul instructed Timothy, who had the gifts and calling of a pastor, to "do the work of an evangelist" (2 Tim. 4:5). He did not mean for Timothy to go from church to church preaching revivals. He meant for Timothy to be intentional about reaching lost people.

- Jesus was intentional in Mark 5, when He went across Galilee to deliver the demoniac of Gadara.
- Jesus was intentional in John 3, when He made Himself available to spend an evening explaining to Nicodemus the new birth.

- Jesus was intentional in John 4, when an outcast at Jacob's well needed someone to give her living water and show her the right way.

- Jesus was intentional on the cross when a dying thief needed forgiveness and life after death.

To be effective, we must focus on intentionality—of schedule, relationships, and people.

4. Build Relationships

The focus here is on "build." Every believer has relationships with an average of twenty unchurched people.

- The lady at the checkout counter in the grocery store
- The neighbor mowing the lawn on Sunday morning when we are on our way to church
- The kid next door who plays in the driveway
- The waitress who regularly serves us lunch
- The guy at the laundry
- The construction workers who build our churches
- The girl at the gas station who takes our money

Soulwinner Leonard Albert refers to these people as FRANs: friends, relatives, associates, and neighbors.

How can we build relationships with the unchurched?

- *Love*. Love is a decision, not an emotion.
- *Learn*. When he said, "Every man I meet is my superior," Will Rogers meant that every person had skills and knowledge he did not have. You can learn something from everyone.

- *Lift*. Lifting is about relating and encouraging, not condescending and lecturing.

- *Look*. Look for doors providentially opened by the Holy Spirit.

I am not surprised to read that over 80 percent of believers are saved because of the influence of a friend or relative. Relationships are essential!

5. Share Christ

Dean Merrill wrote *Sinners in the Hands of an Angry Church*. In it, he talks about how many in the Church seem angry, frustrated, and judgmental, with an axe to grind.

The early church was not angry, they were joyful! Their mission was to preach the Gospel, the "good news." (This word appears more than 100 times in the New Testament.) What was the good news? Jesus Christ! They discovered that sharing Christ was easy.

We must be tactful. Evangelism isn't an assault or a takedown by the "God squad." Witnessing isn't a spiritual mugging where you shove the Gospel down people's throats. In-your-face tactics never seem to work for long in evangelism. Be polite, tactful, and gracious.

Too many believers throw in the towel if they don't see instant results. We must remember the principle of sowing and reaping: "He who sows sparingly will also reap sparingly, and he who sows bountifully will also reap bountifully" (2 Cor. 9:5). This principle is seen in so many areas of life:

- In sales, the ratio of success is often one sale for every nine calls.

- In acting, the ratio can be as high as one job out of thirty auditions, even for successful actors.

- In Jesus' parable of the sower, only one out of four produced favorable results.

Successful people in different walks of life understand the key to success: It is to increase their efforts.

The conclusion for us is obvious: If we desire to *reap* more, we must be willing to *sow* more by sharing Christ more! Many people fail in the area of evangelism because they "sow sparingly" and get discouraged by the meager results.

The people at Antioch were on a mission from God. Here are some ways we can share Christ:

- Share Christ with your neighbor.

- Encourage a fellow believer.

- Pick up litter from your church's sidewalk.

- Shake the hand of a first-time attender.

- Invite an unchurched friend to worship.

- Teach a child.

- Show up for prayer meeting.

- Phone someone to say, "I missed you in church Sunday."

- Volunteer for a Saturday workday.

- Pray for a missionary.

- Practice a song.

- Drop your tithe into the collection.

- Chaperone a youth trip.

- Visit a shut-in.

- Remind yourself you are a missionary on a mission for Christ.

A great church is an evangelistic church that increases its level of sharing Christ, and watches the level of reaping a harvest of souls rise proportionately.

Meditating on the Message

1. Who is the most important person in leading a congregation to becoming an evangelistic church? On what do you base your conclusion?

2. In Jesus' stories of the lost sheep, the lost coin, and the lost son in Luke 15, consider the methods used to reach the lost. Relate these methods to church health. What causes churches to die? Discuss the five steps to evangelistic action.

3. Discuss the various methods of personal witnessing. Which one do you think is most effective in your community?

Assignment: Which method of personal witnessing do you think "fits" your personality? How can we be intentional in witnessing?

Chapter 5

A Great Church Is an Anointed Church

Welcome to the "Acts of the Holy Spirit"! Be sure your seatbelts are properly fastened and your seat backs and tray tables are in their upright and locked positions. From the moment you enter chapter 1 until you exit the to-be-continued last verse of chapter 28, you will be inspired by a journey like no other in the Bible. Stranger than fiction, more spellbinding than a novel, more moving than a biography, Acts is jam-packed with 33 years of Holy Spirit impact.

It is officially called the *Acts of the Apostles*, but once you make the awe-inspiring trip, you'll discover it to be the *Acts of the Holy Spirit,* with responses from the apostles!

In Acts, great churches dot the landscape like light points against the backdrop of night. What made them great? It could not have been their size, structure, skill, or situation.

> They met in houses (Acts 5:42).
>
> Their leaders had limited education (4:13).
>
> Their organization was minimal (2:14).
>
> They faced racism (10:15).
>
> They battled cynicism (5:17; 17:5).
>
> They wrestled with legalism (15:1-2).
>
> They tackled paganism (17:22-23).
>
> They dealt with superstition (14:11).
>
> They confronted witchcraft (19:19).
>
> What's more, they did all this with limited financial resources (4:32).

THE KEY TO GREATNESS

The reason for their greatness was not a secret; they all knew the answer. Unfold the story of their quest, and you will see the answer as plain as day. He, the Holy Spirit, was the answer! Mentioned 56 times in 28 chapters, the Holy Spirit is the central character, not Paul or Peter or Barnabas or James.

These great churches had the Holy Spirit because He had them. The defining phrase of the book could be 15:28: "It seemed good to the Holy Spirit and to us." Just as the Spirit of the Lord was upon Jesus, anointing Him (Luke 4:18), so the Holy Spirit was upon the body of Christ, the believers, anointing them.

Remember Antioch? That's right, it was great because it was a Holy Spirit-anointed church. The very existence of the church at Antioch was due to the Holy Spirit and His anointing.

Before there was a church in that city of a half-million residents, the Holy Spirit brooded over the people. He stirred their hearts, preparing them for unnamed men whom He would send from Cyprus and Cyrene. Their presence in Antioch was as Jesus had predicted.

> You shall receive power when the Holy Spirit has come upon you; and you shall be witnesses to Me . . . to the end of the earth (Acts 1:8).

The first converts at Antioch were the result of the work of the Holy Spirit. Acts 11:20 says that men from Cyprus and Cyrene "spoke to the Hellenists, preaching the Lord Jesus." They could not have said "Jesus is Lord" convincingly, except by the Holy Spirit (1 Cor. 12:3).

Once the people heard about Jesus, the Holy Spirit confirmed His mission. He illuminated their spirits and minds to the truth (John 15:26). The Holy Spirit convicted them of their sins (16:8). Acts 11:21 reveals more: "A great number believed and turned to the Lord."

What happened? They were born again.

"Most assuredly, I say to you, unless one is born of water and the Spirit, he cannot enter the kingdom of God. That which is born of the flesh is flesh, and that which is born of the Spirit is spirit" (John 3:5-6).

THE SIGNIFICANCE OF ANOINTING

Think of Antioch's first pastor. His given name was Joses, but the transforming influence of the Holy Spirit's anointing was so apparent in his life that the apostles nicknamed him Barnabas (Acts 4:36). *Barnabas* meant "son of consolation." In Greek, his name is "son of *Paracletos*," the word Jesus used to describe the Holy Spirit. He spoke of the Paraclete, "one who comes alongside" (see John 14:16-17; see also 15:26). Acts 11:24 emphasizes that Barnabas was "a good man, full of the Holy Spirit and of faith."

Believers at Antioch were obviously anointed by the Holy Spirit. Verses 28-30 say they received, confirmed and responded to a prophetic word given "by the Spirit" regarding a future famine. Clearly, the anointing made the difference in the church at Antioch.

The act of anointing in the Bible was both practically and spiritually significant. The word is used in various tenses over 160 times in both Testaments. *To anoint* simply meant "to rub in, smear on, or pour over."

The first act of anointing occurred when Jacob poured oil on top of a stone at Bethel, confirming a vow he was making to God (Gen. 28:18; 31:13). Practically, anointing was a part of everyday Eastern life.

No Church Left Behind

- Women were anointed for both cosmetic and beautifying purposes (Ruth 3:3; Amos 6:6).

- Hosts would anoint certain guests to symbolize honor and respect (2 Chron. 28:15; Luke 7:44-46).

- The sick and wounded were often anointed with oil and wine for medicinal and healing purposes (Luke 10:34).

- The dead were anointed with oil and various spices for embalming (Mark 14:8; 16:1).

Spiritually, anointing became profoundly significant. High priests, priests, kings, and prophets were anointed (see Ex. 40:13, 15; Num. 35:25; Lev. 4:3; 1 Sam. 9:16; 1 Chron. 11:3; 1 Kings 19:16). Buildings, altars, utensils, furnishings, and other articles were anointed (Ex. 30:26; Num. 7:1).

Jesus' grand entrance into the New Testament story added significance to anointing. The name *Christ* means "anointed one." Jesus was anointing personified.

- Reading Isaiah's prophecy in Luke 4:18, Jesus declared: "The Spirit of the Lord is upon Me, because He has anointed Me."

- Peter's description was, "God anointed Jesus of Nazareth with the Holy Spirit and with power, who went about doing good and healing all who were oppressed by the devil, for God was with Him" (Acts 10:38).

- In picturesque prayer language, Hebrews speaks of Jesus Christ: "Therefore God, Your God, has anointed You with the oil of gladness more than Your companions" (1:9).

What Is the Anointing?

Christ is *the* Anointed One. Believers are *His* anointed ones. "Now He who establishes us with you in Christ and has anointed us is God" (2 Cor. 1:21). John wrote, "But you have an anointing from the Holy One. . . . But the anointing which you have received from Him abides in you" (1 John 2:20, 27).

Bottom line? The church is *His anointed body.* The anointing is so multidimensional it defies simple definition. This is a description:

> The anointing is the selection, sanctification, and sanction of God, expressing the closeness, confirmation, and consecration of Christ, which provides supernatural authority and ability to accomplish the ministry of the Church by the Holy Spirit.

In a personal conversation, Steve Franklin—Bible scholar, teacher, founder and president of Covenant Heirs International—said the following:

> The anointing is supernatural ability for a specialized assignment. Every believer has a specialized assignment (calling). Where your assignment is, is where your anointing will be greatest. Where your anointing is, is where your fulfillment will be greatest. Your anointing is your "unfair advantage" over the enemy, obstacles and threatening circumstances.

> A lot of people fail to find true spiritual fulfillment in life because they try to copy or compete with other believers' anointing and assignments instead of discerning and developing their own.

Perhaps you are thinking, *Okay, if every believer has an anointing, why isn't every local congregation a great, anointed church?* Excellent question! The Bible answers it with this phrase from 1 John 2:27: "The anointing which you have received from Him abides in you." Think about it.

Before the anointing can be received, it must be believed. Like the baptism in the Holy Spirit and other spiritual enablements, anointing must be received by faith. I must believe in the anointing and that it is for me—the average everyday Christian!

The problem is that too many Christians don't really believe they are anointed. Listen to a lot of the teaching about anointing and you'll notice it is tied to the platform, not released in the pew. Spiritual celebrities, prominent personalities, gifted evangelists, and outstanding leaders are "anointed," but little is said about those who, unheralded, carry out the ministry of the local church.

The anointing of the Holy Spirit is not the same as passion, emotion, volume, or physical demonstration. It might include some or all of those things, but it is not limited to them. The anointing "abides in you."

The word *abides* in verse 27 is the Greek word *meno*. This primary verb means "to stay, continue, dwell, endure, be present, remain, stand, tarry." The anointing you believe and receive abides in you!

It stays with you and stands with you. It dwells in you and endures with you. It continues with you and remains with you . . . 24/7. You are not just anointed at times. You are anointed now. You are anointed all the time, every time; good times and bad times; Sunday, Monday, every day; 3 p.m. or 3 a.m!

What's more, your church needs you to be anointed. It is important not only to you, but also to the body of Christ, to be anointed. Discern your special assignment. Appropriate your anointing. The impetus for greatness in your church abides with you. The anointing in you is the Holy Spirit's anointing. You have an anointing—live with it!

PARADIGMS FOR CHURCH HEALTH

This is what the saints at Antioch did. The Holy Spirit anointing was active and productive. Study the amazing effects of the Holy Spirit at Antioch and you can't help but be struck with the healthy results.

Think about it. When Jesus sent out His twelve disciples two-by-two, "they . . . anointed with oil many who were sick, and healed them" (Mark 6:13). Years later, James instructed the elders of the church to anoint the sick with oil and pray for their healing (James 5:14-15). *There is a clear connection between anointing and health.*

Likewise, there is a direct correlation between the anointing of the Holy Spirit and a healthy church. The Holy Spirit yearns to build great, effective, and healthy churches.

The last half of the twentieth century saw much activity, research, and writing on the subject of church growth. Elmer Towns, Donald McGavran, Peter Wagner, and Win Arn, among others, were pioneers. Thousands of churches became better equipped because of the principles and practices advanced by the movement. During the 1990s, the "church growth movement" began to evolve into a "church health movement."

Using the knowledge of church growth and adding the dimension of church health, the Church today is better able to reach and disciple the end-time harvest. These helps are the work of the Holy Spirit.

The church-health paradigm is simple: When a church is healthy, it will grow. Church health is focused more on people and ministry than on numbers and diagnosis. Every church in any setting can strive for health, because true greatness only comes to a healthy church.

At this point, things begin to get a bit sticky, because there are as many characteristics of a healthy church as there are sources that describe them. Mark Dever wrote an excellent article in *Ministries Today* called "Prescription for a Healthy Church." In it, he provided a sampling of perspectives from eighteen different sources. Here are six of them, including Dever's own list. As you read, identify the areas of your own church's health.

Darrel Robinson

- Vision
- Commitment
- Leadership
- Unity
- Membership involvement
- Celebrative and joyful worship and praise
- Prayer
- Fellowship
- Organization
- Equipping
- Pastoral care and ministry
- Evangelizing[1]

Rick Warren

- *Worship*: Loving the Lord with all your heart, magnifying Him, makes the church grow stronger.

- *Ministry*: Loving your neighbor as yourself makes the church grow broader.

- *Evangelism*: Making disciples, staying on mission, makes the church grow larger.

- *Fellowship*: Baptizing believers, increasing membership, makes the church grow warmer.

- *Discipleship*: Teaching them to obey and helping them mature makes the church grow deeper.[2]

George Barna

- Win people to Christ.
- Raise Bible knowledge.
- Equip the Christian body.
- Establish Christian community.
- Renew Christian behavior.
- Enhance the image of the local church.
- Champion Christian morals.
- Live by a Christian philosophy of life.
- Restore people's self-esteem.
- Focus on reaching the world for Christ.[3]

Mark Shaw

- Truth (Martin Luther)
- Spirituality (John Calvin)
- Unity (Jeremiah Burroughs)
- Assurance (William Perkins)
- Worship (Richard Baxter)
- Renewal (Jonathan Edwards)
- Growth (John Wesley)
- Love for the lost (William Carey)

- Justice (William Wilberforce)
- Fellowship (Dietrich Bonhoeffer)[4]

Leith Anderson

- Sensing the presence of God
- Others-centered
- Understanding terminology
- People who look like me
- Healthy problem handling
- Accessibility
- Sense of expectation[5]

Mark Dever

- Expositional preaching
- Biblical theology
- The Gospel
- Biblical understanding of conversion
- Biblical understanding of evangelism
- Biblical understanding of church membership
- Biblical church discipline
- Concern for discipleship and growth
- Biblical church leadership[6]

Setting Your Course

Earlier, I mentioned Dr. Dan Reiland (by the way, I'm still mad at him). In evaluating the health of Metropolitan Church of God in Birmingham, Alabama, he used the "Nine Leading Qualities of a Healthy Church." I shared Dan's findings with our staff, elders, and leaders, and found them to be extremely helpful.

1. Servant-hearted spiritual leadership
2. Vibrant spirituality
3. Global-local evangelism
4. Intentional disciple-making
5. Gift-based empowered ministry
6. Healthy and loving relationships
7. Wise and generous financial stewardship
8. Uplifting worship services
9. Christian community within small groups

Earlier I described the anointing of the Holy Spirit as . . .

> The selection, sanctification, and sanction of God expressing the closeness, confirmation, and consecration of Christ, which provides supernatural authority and ability to accomplish the ministry of the Church by the Holy Spirit.

The anointing must be believed and received. When this happens, the abiding authority and ability of the Holy Spirit will be the catalyst for the development of church health.

The anointing makes the difference, but we must make the effort. Health follows anointing. We will discuss the qualities necessary for a healthy church in chapter 7.

MEDITATING ON THE MESSAGE

1. What are four occasions when "anointing" played a significant role in the lives of Eastern peoples?

2. Why was Jesus anointed for ministry? Who is the "Anointed One"? Why is the Church called "His anointed body"?

3. Discuss how greatness can come only to an anointed church.

Assignment: Healthy growth marks from seven different church-growth experts are listed in this chapter. What can you do to promote spiritual health in your church?

A Great Church Is an Anointed Church

Chapter 6

A Great Church Is a Tenacious Church

His given name was Joses. The apostles gave him the nickname *Barnabas*, which means "son of encouragement." When we read the case study of the church in Antioch, we understand why.

On Barnabas' first visit to the city on the Orontes River, he saw the grace of God on an infant church. The only exhortation specifically credited to him in the entire narrative was an encouragement to persevere. He "encouraged them all that with purpose of heart they should continue with the Lord" (Acts 11:23).

- Keep on keeping on!
- Don't quit!

- Hang in there!

- Don't give up!

- The best is yet to come!

Barnabas could not know the effect his words had on those believers. New Testament scholar French Arrington says the church endured into the fourth or fifth century. That's four to five times longer than the average life span of historical Christian churches. A church cannot truly be considered a great church without longevity produced by tenacity. They are always handing off the baton to the next generation in the race before them.

The jury is still out on many of the churches in America that have been declared "great" churches. One-year, two-year, three-year assessments pale in contrast to the importance of our children and our children's children. Great churches are transgenerational. Great churches are tenacious.

During my years as a pastor, I saw more than a few churches blow into our city, blow up and blow out. Today, they are gone—brief flashes in the pan of time—their influence and their witness embarrassingly extinguished.

You have seen the same thing in your town if you have lived there more than five years. Missiologist Lyle Schaller tells us we are closing more than 13,000 Evangelical churches every year in America, while planting only 5,100. North America is the only continent on earth where the church is not growing.

In one of his short stories, Frank O'Connor tells of the times he and his boyhood friends would run through orchards of Ireland. As they ran across the fields, they would come to an orchard wall that seemed to stretch too far to go around and looked too high to climb. The boys would simply *throw their hats over the wall, leaving no option but to find a way to follow.*

With 8,000 American churches quitting the race every year, someone ought to throw a hat over the wall! Two walls challenge our tenacity. One is natural and developmental; the other is supernatural and destructive. We must find ways to overcome these walls.

THE WALL OF RESISTANCE

One major wall is the wall of resistance. Individuals, corporations, churches, even sports teams experience it all the time. Life comes "standard-equipped" with resistance. Behind every success story you will find the story of a struggle.

Go back to the pristine innocence of the Creation story in Genesis 1 and 2. God's instructions to Adam and Eve included three revealing words: *subdue, tend,* and *keep* (1:28; 2:15). Each word carries in it the principle of resistance. Remember, this was before the Serpent, sin, or the fallout of the Fall. The idyllic setting of a God-planted garden held the undercurrent of God-ordained resistance.

Study the history of Israel, and you will discover the continuing principle of resistance. God gave Canaan to Israel.

When they entered the land, however, the guiding pillars of fire and cloud disappeared, and the miracle manna ceased.

After an easy victory at Jericho, Israel had to conquer every inch of ground she gained in the conquest of the land. Resistance. No wonder the Lord's instructions were so specific: "Go in to *possess* the land which the Lord your God is giving you to *possess*" (Josh. 1:11, emphasis mine).

Perhaps this is why the command to be strong is repeated four times in Joshua 1 (vv. 6, 7, 9, 18), and appears over 300 times in the Old Testament. First Samuel 30:6 says, "David strengthened himself in the Lord." This literally means he "made himself strong in the Lord."

Look at the resistance faced by the early church. Five hundred brethren at one time saw the resurrected Christ (1 Cor. 15:6), yet only a fourth of them showed up in the Upper Room for prayer meeting (Acts 1:15).

After the 120 left the Upper Room, they faced mocking (2:13); a lame man was healed and the church leaders were threatened (4:3); a bit later, two church members turned out to be liars (5:3); and the Hellenist believers began a complaint campaign (6:1). Have you ever heard of a church like this?

You get the picture! Resistance has been hardwired into the human equation. We cannot simply mark it off as spiritual warfare, because Adam and Eve faced it in the pre-Serpent Garden of Eden.

Why does the Lord permit resistance, or perhaps even ordain it? I can't speak for God, but I can observe His actions. He took a resistant world that was void and without form, shrouded in darkness, and created what He called "good." He took lifeless dust, breathed life into it and called it "very good" (Gen. 1:10, 31).

The Bible calls what God did "work" (2:2). So God is a worker, and He willed that His ultimate creation bear the work aspect of His image (see also Gen. 2:8; Pss. 8:3; 111:3; John 9:4; 1 Cor. 3:9; 2 Thess. 3:10). Work is about overcoming resistance. There are many reasons why God uses resistance:

- Without resistance, there would be no work; without work, there would be no development.
- Resistance creates improvement through labor.
- Resistance motivates tenacity.
- Resistance enhances development of personal skills.
- It releases God-given gifts of creativity.
- It catalyzes discovery, invention, and progress.
- It beautifies our lives with meaning and fulfillment.
- It enlarges the depth and breadth of our character.
- It purifies our motives.
- It is a gateway to discipline and achievement.
- It reminds us of our dependence on the Creator.
- It defines faithfulness.
- It prepares us for spiritual conflict.

Through resistance, we grow our way to a healthy church. If we know this, why are we so intimidated by resistance? Why do we take it so personally? Why do we think about quitting? Why do we feel so isolated? Why do we doubt God's purpose for our lives? Why do we resign to failure? The road to success in any area of life is uphill all the way. I need to be reminded at times that I'm not the Lone Ranger. Everyone faces resistance:

- Einstein was four years old before he could speak, and seven before he read.
- Isaac Newton did poorly in grade school.
- John Milton was blind.
- Beethoven was deaf.
- Thomas Edison was told by his teachers he was too stupid to learn.
- F. W. Woolworth was told by his employers at a dry-goods store that he "didn't have enough sense" to wait on customers.
- A newspaper editor fired Walt Disney because he had no good ideas.
- Caruso's music teacher told him, "You can't sing."
- Leo Tolstoy flunked out of college.
- Michael Jordan was cut from his high school basketball team.
- Dr. Suess' first book was rejected by twenty-seven publishers.

- Rudyard Kipling was told by the editor at *The San Francisco Examiner*, "You don't know how to use the English language.

- John Bunyan wrote *Pilgrim's Progress* from Bedford Prison.

- Sir Walter Raleigh wrote his *History of the World* during a thirteen-year imprisonment.

- Martin Luther translated the Bible while confined in the castle at Wartburg.

- The apostle Paul wrote five books of the Bible from prison.

We need to remind ourselves that every church—big/small, urban/suburban, rich/poor, north/south, east/west—deals with resistance. There are . . .

- Disappointing attendances
- Money shortages
- Clogged toilets
- Parking problems
- Leaking roofs
- Doubting Thomases
- Rising utilities
- Space limitations
- Spoiled saints
- Hard decisions
- Zoning problems

- Building crises
- Empty pews
- Stormy weekends
- Resigning leaders
- Insufficient laborers.

Let's make an advance decision to throw our hats over the wall, leaving no option but to follow. There is no testimony without a test, no miracle without a mess, no triumph without tenacity. Our children and grandchildren are depending on us. God is with us. If we will not quit, we cannot be stopped.

Don't Quit

When things go wrong, as they sometimes will,
When the road you're trudging seems all uphill,
When the funds are low and the debts are high,
And you want to smile, but you have to sigh,
When care is pressing you down a bit,
Rest if you must, but don't you quit.

Life is queer with its twists and turns,
As every one of us sometimes learns,
And many a failure turns about
When he might have won had he stuck it out;
Don't give up, though the pace seems slow;
You might succeed with another blow.
Often the goal is nearer than
It seems to a faint and faltering man,
Often the struggler has given up
When he might have captured the victor's cup.

And he learned too late, when the night slipped down,
How close he was to the golden crown.

Success is failure turned inside out;
The silver tint of the clouds of doubt.
And you never can tell how close you are;
It may be near when it seems afar.
So stick to the fight when you're hardest hit;
It's when things seem worst that you mustn't quit.

For we know the Father above looks down,
He sees our struggles and holds a crown.
He knows the way, though it's rough and drear;
He will give us strength, so we need not fear.
He offers to you the refreshing cup
Of the water of life; so in faith, look up.
So struggle on 'til the crown is won,
Which He will give when our work is done.

—Author Unknown

THE WALL OF CONFLICT WITH SATAN

The second wall faced by the Church is more daunting. Its intent is not to resist but to prevail against. Hinged on this wall are what Jesus called "the gates of hell" in the King James Version (Matt. 16:18). The actual word Jesus used for *hell* was *hades*: the gates of hades shall not prevail against Christ's church.

The word *hades* is used in Scripture to refer to the unseen, invisible, or spiritual world. From this invisible reality, opposition to the Church launches its foul schemes. The *gates of hell* is not some free-floating influence in a vacuum. The gates have a single, diabolical source in Satan himself. Hell's gates represent Satan's strategy aimed at stopping the advancing Church.

The result is a conflict more far-reaching than we can imagine, more immediate than the War on Terror.

The Reality of the Conflict

Christ sends His representatives out as sheep surrounded by wolves (Matt. 10:16). Further, He warns us that we are up against the "father of lies," a "thief," and "the god of this age" (John 8:44 NIV; 10:10; 2 Cor. 4:4). Our Enemy is real (Isa. 24:12-14; Ezek. 28:12-19). His organization is real; it consists of powers, principalities, rulers of darkness, and spiritual wickedness (Eph. 6:12).

To deny conflict is like trying to deny the law of gravity, the four seasons, sunrise or sunset. *To ignore conflict* is like skipping through the worst part of town, flashing hundred-dollar bills, or strolling into Iran wearing an "I love America" T-shirt.

To be preoccupied with conflict, looking for a demon behind every door, is to be driven by a paranoia that blinds us to the harvest before us. *To surrender to conflict* is to leave our families and churches vulnerable to the opposing forces of Satan's "axis of evil."

Be sober, be vigilant; because your adversary the devil walks about like a roaring lion, seeking whom he may devour (1 Peter 5:8).

The Rationale of the Conflict

Warfare is mentioned in the New Testament seventeen times. Three of the seventeen are about military war; eight of the seventeen are related to the Book of Revelation. The remaining six references to warfare are as follows:

1. Mental bondage (2 Cor. 10:3-5)
2. Warring a good warfare (1 Tim. 1:18)
3. Warfare's distracting entanglements (2 Tim. 2:4)
4. Pleasure desires battling in our bodies (James 4:1)
5. Fighting among ourselves (v. 2)
6. Fleshly lusts that war against us (1 Peter 2:11)

Here's the shocker: The devil is not mentioned a single time in these six references! But isn't conflict about Satan? Aren't we in a war with him? Indeed. Doesn't he oppose? Of course.

In fact, he opposes all men, women, and children on earth because they are made in God's image and Christ died to redeem them.

Aren't we in a spiritual war? Yes. Doesn't Satan make a frontal assault against us? Absolutely!

He uses "shock and awe" to overwhelm; guerrilla attacks to slow our advance; propaganda campaigns to deceive; terror plots to intimidate.

Here is the kicker: All of Satan's tactics are focused on influencing our minds. Satan's aim is to get between our ears. Once he has a foothold, he uses deception, denial, division, duplicity, and discouragement to defeat us.

This is why the Bible says a person is what he thinks (see Prov. 23:7). Hosea reminds us that people are destroyed because they lack knowledge (4:6).

Paul writes that we are not ignorant of Satan's devices (2 Cor. 2:11). The word *devices* means thoughts and strategies. Romans 8:6 declares that "to be carnally minded is death, but to be spiritually minded is life and peace."

This is why the Bible tells us we must live with renewed minds (12:2; Eph. 4:23). Two words in 2 Corinthians 10:3-5 are particularly important in understanding Satan's rationale in influencing the mind:

> For though we walk in the flesh, we do not war according to the flesh. For the weapons of our warfare are not carnal but mighty in God for pulling down *strongholds*, casting down *arguments* and every high thing that exalts itself against the knowledge of God, bringing every thought into captivity to the obedience of Christ.

Strongholds. These are fortresses, secure places, castles of the mind. The Enemy acts as a sniper in a tower to shoot down faith, hope, love, courage, and commitment. These strongholds are often built on the grounds of bitterness, prejudice, bad habits, abuse, fear, and anger. We must recognize them and pull them down, using spiritual weapons.

Arguments ("imaginations," KJV). This is a debate term that had roots in the Greek period, but was well known in the first century. Philosophers like Plato and Aristotle used this technique while debating ideas, truth, life, and the senses. Here's how Satan uses debate in our minds:

- *First,* he gives us his agenda.
- *Second,* he attacks unrelentingly to get us to accept his agenda as true.
- *Third,* Satan resorts to diatribe to beat us down.

Arguments of Satan tell us our marriage will fail and our dreams will die. He tries to convince us that we are not saved and God doesn't hear our prayers. At first we think the worst. We'll die young. Our church can't grow. God is not enough.

Don't buy into Satan's arguments. We must cast them down, using spiritual weapons.

Our Response to the Conflict

We must be tenacious. When Ephesians 4:27 advises us to give no place to the devil, it is telling us to not give up gained ground. The conflict is taking place in *our* territory— it's called heavenly places! Study Ephesians and you'll see the happenings of heavenly places:

- In heavenly places we are blessed with every spiritual blessing in Christ (1:3).
- In heavenly places Christ is seated at the right hand of the Father (v. 20).

- In heavenly places we have been raised to sit with Christ (2:6).

- In heavenly places the manifold wisdom of God is made known by the Church to principalities and powers (3:10).

- In heavenly places we wrestle against principalities, powers, rulers of darkness, and spiritual wickedness (6:12).

Heavenly places is where we are blessed, where Christ is seated, where we sit with Christ, where the Church reveals God's multicolored wisdom, and where we wrestle with evil.

Get it? You and I—the Church—have home-field advantage! Do you see it? This conflict is fought on God's turf. We have been declared heirs of God and joint-heirs with Christ (Rom. 8:17). We do not fight as victims, but as victors!

God equips us to be tenacious. We have the belt of truth, the breastplate of righteousness, the shoes of readiness, the shield of faith, the helmet of salvation, the sword of the Spirit, and the gift of praying in the Spirit (Eph. 6:13-18). Inventory your assets. List your weapons of warfare:

- The blood of Jesus Christ (Rev. 12:11)

- The Word of God (Luke 4:4, 8, 12; Heb. 4:12)

- Intercession (Acts 12:5)

- Angelic activity (Dan. 10:13; Rev. 12:9-11)

- Symbolic action (2 Kings 19:14; Josh. 6:15)

- Prayer (Acts 6:1-4)

- Fasting (Isa. 58:6)
- Seeking God (Jer. 29:12-14)
- Praise (Ps. 149:6-9)
- Asserting authority (Mark 11:20-24)
- Knowledge of Satan (2 Cor. 2:11)
- Christ's example (Luke 11:21-22)
- Believers' testimony (Rev. 12:11)
- Commanding (Acts 16:18)
- Tears (Ps. 126:1-6)
- Faith (1 John 5:4)
- Standing (Eph. 6:10)
- The anointing (Isa. 10:27)
- Seeing the invisible (2 Kings 6:8-17)
- Self-control (1 Peter 5:8)
- Vigilance (v. 8)
- Sounding an alarm (Num. 10:9)
- Submission to God (James 4:7)
- Resisting the devil (1 Peter 5:9)
- The Lord's rebuke (Zech. 3:1-2; Jude 9)
- Spiritual experiences (Heb. 5:14)
- Spiritual discernment (1 Cor. 12:10)

The bottom line is that we are more than conquerors!

The Reason for the Conflict

Why do we have conflict if the Cross disarms principalities and powers, making them a public spectacle, triumphing over them (Col. 2:15)? Why, if through death, Jesus destroyed the devil who had the power of death (Heb. 2:14)? Why, if Christ was manifested for the purpose of destroying the works of the devil (1 John 3:8)?

The answer is revealed in 1 Corinthians 15. Indeed, Jesus won the victory at the Cross and validated it by His resurrection! He delegated authority to His church to evangelize the lost and enforce the victory (Matt. 28:18-20). From the Cross to the end of time, the victory must be enforced. Christ won the victory. His church is here to enforce it until the end comes.

> Then comes the end, when He delivers the kingdom to God the Father, when He puts an end to all rule and all authority and power. For He must reign till He has put all enemies under His feet. The last enemy that will be destroyed is death. For "He has put all things under His feet." But when He says "all things are put under Him," it is evident that He who put all things under Him is excepted. Now when all things are made subject to Him, then the Son Himself will also be subject to Him who put all things under Him, that God may be all in all (1 Cor. 15:24-28).

This is why the encouraging words of Barnabas to the church at Antioch still ring true for the twenty-first-century church. With purpose of heart, we must continue with the

Lord (Acts 11:23). There will be ultimate triumph because of undying tenacity.

Those who went before us realized this and threw their hats over the walls of resistance and satanic opposition, leaving no option but for us to follow.

William Wilberforce was elected to the English House of Commons at the age of twenty-one. At age twenty-five, he was saved. His best friend, Prime Minister William Pitt, challenged him, "England needs a crusade to stop the horrible slave trade. The Lord has raised you up for the Church and the nation. It will be a long fight, but you are the man!"

Sensing God's approval, Wilberforce committed his life to Christian freedom. Over a twenty-year period, he had nineteen emancipation bills voted down. For forty-nine years he tenaciously endured derision, rejection, and threats against his life. On his deathbed, however, he received word that the House of Commons had passed his emancipation bill. A month later, the House of Lords passed it, and the slaves were freed in Great Britain!

John Wesley, ordained at twenty-four, ministered for sixty-four years. He preached 42,400 sermons (fifteen-per-week average for fifty-four years), traveled 290,000 miles on horseback and wrote 200 volumes of books. When he died at eighty-eight, he left behind only a worn-out coat, a battered hat, a humble cottage, a tattered Bible, and . . . the Methodist Church!

Willard Hotchkiss had thirty-nine bouts with malaria and was attacked by lions three times. When he died, he said, "I would do it all over again for the privilege of shining the light of the Savior into a dark world."

Dr. John Geddie went to Aneityum in 1848 to reach the cannibals. During the next six years he preached the Gospel, developed an alphabet, translated the New Testament, and led more than half of the 4,000-plus inhabitants to Christ. For twenty-four years he tenaciously gave himself to God's cause. When he died, the people erected a monument in his memory, inscribed with these words:

> When he landed in 1848, there were no Christians.
>
> When he left in 1872, there were no heathens.

Look closely and you will find that great churches have the same DNA. With purpose of heart, they continue with the Lord. Left-behind churches, however, override their spiritual DNA and settle down to being a *good* church but not a *great* one. Their pedigree is excellent, their reputation is flawless, but they never become a great church.

Greatness escapes them. Tenacity eludes them.

You and I agree, however: We don't want to be left behind! To excel, we must be tenacious. We will explore how in the next chapter.

MEDITATING ON THE MESSAGE

1. What are some benefits derived from conquering the "wall" of natural resistance?

2. Identify something in your contemporary experience or in the Church that illustrates the "wall of resistance."

3. Look up the six references to spiritual warfare given in this chapter. Read the context of each scripture, and ask God to give the congregation special insight for living in the Spirit and growing a thriving local church.

Assignment: Discuss some things your church can do to move it from being a good church to a great one.

Chapter 7

Ten Marks of
a Healthy Church

Let's do a case study of the church at Antioch. You will be
inspired to see the health indicators in this anointed
congregation. Acts 11:19-26 provides an overview of the
story, while 13:1-4 gives us some insight into this church. In
order to do this, let us look at ten marks of a healthy church
that were evident at Antioch.

1. Spiritual Gifts Were
Demonstrated

Prophets came.... One of them ... stood up and
showed by the Spirit that there was going to be a
great famine throughout the world (Acts 11:27-28).

> Now in the church that was at Antioch there were certain prophets and teachers (13:1).

The church at Antioch was gifted. So is your church. An anointed church already has the gifts it needs when it needs them, because the Holy Spirit is the Giver. Limitless resources of the Holy Spirit provide unlimited resources to the Church. As we unwrap, develop, and deploy these gifts, the Church grows and becomes more healthy.

The Bible presents three groups of spiritual gifts. *First*, there are the ministry gifts, which provide leadership and equipping. They are apostles, prophets, evangelists, pastors, and teachers (Eph. 4:11-16).

Second, motivation gifts build and bless. Among these gifts are faith, prophecy, serving, teaching, exhorting, giving, hospitality, administration, intercession, leading, mercy, and so forth (Rom. 12:3-13; 16:1-2; 1 Cor. 7:7-8; 9:19-23; 1 Tim. 2:1-2; 5:17).

Third, manifestation gifts are given for power and spontaneity. These gifts reside permanently in the Holy Spirit, not in the believer. They are manifested spontaneously as the Holy Spirit wills. There are nine of these manifestation gifts, according to 1 Corinthians 12:7-11:

- The *word of wisdom* is a specific insight or application God gives to someone, a word to unify and build up individuals as well as the entire local body of Christ.

- The *word of knowledge* is an ability God gives certain believers to receive a direct word from God, revealing accurate information and ideas pertaining to the local church or to an individual believer.

- The *gift of faith* is a special ability the Holy Spirit gives individuals to believe with extraordinary confidence the will and purposes of God.

- The *gift of healings* is a special ability the Holy Spirit gives believers to serve as human instruments to restore health and bring healings, apart from natural means.

- The *gift of miracles* is a special ability the Holy Spirit gives believers to serve as human instruments and perform powerful acts that overrule nature.

- The *gift of prophecy* is a special ability the Holy Spirit gives believers to receive and communicate a direct message from God to people for a specific purpose.

- The *gift of discerning of spirits* is a special ability the Holy Spirit gives believers to know with assurance whether certain behavior is in reality of God, of human origin, or of satanic origin.

- The *gift of tongues* is a special ability the Holy Spirit gives believers to speak in a language they have never learned, and to receive a message in the heavenly language from God and communicate it to people.

- The *gift of interpretation of tongues* is a special ability the Holy Spirit gives believers to make known the message of the one who speaks in tongues.

The quest for health and greatness in a church demands that all believers identify and demonstrate these gifts of the Holy Spirit as a lifestyle. How sad it is to see a church limit the Spirit's gifts to corporate worship.

2. PERSONAL STEWARDSHIP WAS PRACTICED

> The disciples, each according to his ability, determined to send relief to the brethren dwelling in Judea (Acts 11:29).

The word *disciples* in this passage refers to learners, believers, and Christians at Antioch. The phrase "each according to his ability" connotes individual stewardship. The word *relief* means "money." That's right, money was an indicator of the church's health. Obviously, individualized stewardship was a practice.

Stewardship is the management of a household. A steward manages a household's money for the owner. Skills, giftedness, potentiality, intelligence, and even athleticism amount to little without wise management.

Why do some "most likelies" turn out to be mediocre limpers, or worse, miserable losers? Poor management. How can the potentially challenged become high achievers? Excellent management! We do not all have the same qualities, but we all have something. Wise stewardship is the proper management of all our God-given resources for the glory of God.

Stewardship says, "God is the owner, I am the manager. I own nothing, yet I am responsible for everything." When we realize we manage what God owns, the pressure is less, because we have a senior Partner. Wisdom increases because He is the Almighty Adviser.

Decisions are easier because we live by Kingdom principles. The returns are greater because they are His returns. When the Lord owns and we manage, He teaches us because we are His disciples. He trusts us because we are faithful. He touches through us because we become His hands extended.

As able stewards, we are delivered from the spirit of poverty—the attitude that we will never have enough. We overcome the spirit of fear because with Him, what matters is faithfulness. We conquer the spirit of selfishness, knowing we are rivers, not reservoirs. His resources flow *through* us, not just *to* us.

Have you ever wondered why stewardship focuses on money? There is a good reason. Crown Financial Ministries says money and material resources are mentioned in the Bible over 2,300 times. Prayer is mentioned 500 times; faith, 250 times; repentance, 70 times; baptism, 20 times.

Why does God make a big deal over a buck? We realize the answer when we craft a biblical theology of money.

- Money is a character indicator (Luke 16:12).

- Money competes with Christ's lordship (v. 13).

- Money reveals my affection (Matt. 6:21).

- Money management reveals my trustworthiness (Luke 16:11-12).

- Much of life revolves around earning and using money (2 Thess. 3:8).

- Money is neither good nor bad (1 Tim. 6:10).

- Poverty is not necessarily a virtue (Prov. 30:9).

Five Ways to Manage Money

The Bible instructs us to manage money in five simple ways.

1. *Receive gratefully.*

> Both riches and honor come from You, and You reign over all. In Your hand is power and might; in Your hand it is to make great and to give strength to all. Now therefore, our God, we thank You and praise Your glorious name (1 Chron. 29:12-13).

2. *Tithe obediently.* Our great, loving God deserves the firstfruits, not the leftovers (Ex. 23:19). The tithe is . . .

T—a *Tenth* (Deut. 14:22 NLT)

I—an *Investment* (12:6-7)

T—a *Test* (Mal. 3:10 NIV)

H—*Holy* (Lev. 27:30)

E—an *Expression* (Gen. 28:20-22).

3. *Give generously* (Luke 6:38). A truly generous person gives lovingly (1 Cor. 13:3), worshipfully (Num. 18:24), cheerfully (2 Cor. 9:7), graciously (8:7), sacrificially (2 Sam. 24:24).

4. *Save consistently.* The Living Bible says it like this: "The wise man saves for the future, but the foolish man spends whatever he gets" (Prov. 21:20).

5. *Spend wisely* (Isa. 55:2). Spending money is not sinful; aren't you glad? The best things in life may be free, but lunch isn't. What *should* we spend money for?

Shelter

   Provisions

      Enjoyment

         Necessities

            Development

You may have the noblest of visions, but if you do not manage money effectively, they are only pipe dreams. Christian stewardship doesn't happen by raising money; it happens by raising people. During two and a half decades in the pastorate, I realized I was shortchanging the church if I took their money without teaching biblical stewardship.

At first, I was afraid. I was afraid of offending someone, afraid people would question my motives. I was afraid of the daunting task of personal preparation and example. But I learned that people are hungry for total life truth.

I also discovered that one sermon on tithing every other year was not enough. People in a congregation grow best when there is a stewardship series of four to six weeks every twelve to eighteen months. They also need small-group studies and protracted seminars at least annually.

In one of our most repeated seminars, "Getting Your Financial House in Order," we taught how to eliminate debt and maximize resources. Some of our most effective discipleship took place at the wellspring of stewardship.

When God gives a church a vision, He is able to finance it. Visions, however, aren't paid for by big offerings and showmanship. They are underwritten by big people who practice Christian stewardship. Dr. Jack Hyles said it best in a conference I attended many years ago: "Great pastors don't build great churches. Great pastors build great people, and great people build great churches."

3. Healthy Community Was Nurtured

Now in the church that was at Antioch . . . (Acts 13:1).

The city itself was not the church. The church in Antioch was a community of faith, bonded together in the Spirit and anointed by the Holy Ghost. Community? Oh, yes. Believers held in common something dear—commitment to Jesus Christ. They exhibited unity, togetherness, oneness, focus. Thus, there was "common unity," or *community*.

There is unity in community, but there is also diversity. Unity is not uniformity because it does not cancel diversity. The Church must be in unity while promoting diversity. The members of the body are together, yet they function individually in the tasks to which they are gifted and called (1 Cor. 12:17-18).

Members of an orchestra do not play the same instrument or line of music, but they all play the same song.

- Community means we belong to Christ and to one another (Rom. 12:5).
- We motivate one another to love and good deeds (Heb. 10:24-25).
- We are provided a support group to help in times of difficulty (Acts 2:46).
- Racial, cultural, class, and financial barriers are pulled down (Rom. 10:12).
- Accountability and responsibility are practiced (5:12).
- Financial needs of the poor are met (Acts 2:44-45). (Note: Some interpret vv. 44-45 as communism instead of community. Wrong! Communism is about the government owning and dispersing everything; Christian community is when believers hold everything in trust as stewards and give through love as the Holy Spirit leads.)

God's will does not end when we *believe*; He expects us to *belong*. We must move from being a spectator (one who watches, consumes, and benefits without responsibility) to being a participator (involved, sharing, responsible).

When we are saved, we commit to Christ. When we join a local church, we commit to the people of Christ. There are four kinds of people in a community: isolators, insulators, incubators, and "interactors."

People who choose to live in isolation close others out. Isolation is motivated by fear—fear of failure, fear of commitment, fear of personal growth, fear of people, fear of being out of control, fear of responsibility, and fear of accountability.

Those who choose insulation seal themselves in. Insulation is motivated by the pain of disillusionment, disappointment, betrayal, abandonment, rejection, failure—all spilling over from the past. "I've been hurt before, I won't be hurt again," we hear them say. Like a marble, they touch but do not feel.

Those who choose incubation are waiting for an ideal time, place, situation. Motivated by perfectionism, the incubating person often says, "I am not good enough, mature enough, trained enough, experienced enough, or spiritual enough— yet.

Then there are those who choose interaction. Motivated by faith, they see life as an adventure. Unafraid of risks, unwilling to procrastinate and insightful enough to handle hurts, they believe God uses ordinary individuals to make extraordinary differences. The Bible has much to say about interacting with others in the community of faith.

- Wash one another's feet (John 13:14).

- Love one another (vv. 34-35).

- Live in peace with one another (1 Thess. 5:13).

- Honor one another (Phil. 2:3).

- Stop judging one another (Rom. 14:15).

- Accept one another (15:7).

- Teach and admonish one another (v. 14).

- Do not be conceited, provoking and envying one another (Gal. 5:26).

- Restore one another (6:1).

- Bear with one another (Eph. 4:2).

- Be kind to one another (v. 32).

- Sing to one another (5:19-20).

- Submit to one another (v. 21).

- Do not lie to one another (Col. 3:9).

- Comfort and encourage each other (1 Thess. 4:18).

- Spur one another on to good deeds (Heb. 10:24).

- Do not grumble about one another (James 5:9).

- Do not slander one another (4:11).

- Confess your sins to one another (5:16).

- Offer hospitality to one another (1 Peter 4:9).

- Clothe yourselves in humility with one another (5:5).

- Fellowship with one another (1 John 1:7).

Healthy churches nurture community.

4. God-Centered Worship Was Offered

As they ministered to the Lord ... (Acts 13:2).

The ministry of worship at Antioch was clearly focused on the Lord. It was God-centered. Christ described this as "worship in spirit and in truth."

> But the hour is coming, and now is, when the true worshipers will worship the Father in spirit and truth; for the Father is seeking such to worship Him. God is Spirit, and those who worship Him must worship in spirit and truth (John 4:23-24).

The word *spirit*, spelled with the lowercase "s," denotes the inner being of an individual. It relates to the core of personhood. It is the spirit of a person communing with the Spirit of God. It is "deep calling to deep" (see Ps. 42:7).

> The spirit of a man is the lamp of the Lord, searching all the inner depths of his heart (Prov. 20:27).

So the phrase "in spirit" refers to the human spirit—that which bears the image of God (Gen. 2:7; Rom. 1:9). It is worship that is real, not superficial; spiritual, not sensual. It is worship from an undivided heart.

The word *truth* refers to worship based on the revelation of God in His Word (John 17:17; 18:38; Ps. 119:142, 160). Still, all of this is dependent on the ministry of the Holy Spirit (1 Cor. 2:11-12; 12:3).

The most common Greek word for *worship* is *proskuneo*. *Strong's Concordance* (#4352) says it means "to kiss toward, to kiss the hand, to bow down, to prostrate oneself." Thus, worship shows sincere affection, relates to God with honor, approaches God with a submissive attitude, and encounters God with awestruck humility. Is your worship God-centered? Do you worship Him in spirit and in truth? Does God get anything out of your worship? Do you bless God, or seek only to be blessed?

Let's clear the air: God-centered worship is not "bless me"; it is "bless Thee." It is not a human means to a self-centered end. God-centered worship is not a church-growth tool. It is not a feel-good exercise. It is not an excuse for fleshly display. Worship is not a preliminary to preaching. It is not a replacement for the Word. It is not a form of escapism. It is not limited to singing.

Self-centered worship is unacceptable to God. Worship focused on self is, at best, misguided; and at worst, idolatrous. No wonder the church at Antioch enjoyed health, they decentralized themselves and exalted their God.

5. Fasting Was Practiced

> As they ministered to the Lord and fasted. . . . Then, having fasted . . . (Acts 13:2-3).

Fasting is mentioned two times in the first twelve chapters of Acts. Paul fasted after his Damascus-road conversion (9:9), and Cornelius fasted before his conversion (10:30). The next occasion was 13:2-3, when leaders of the church at Antioch fasted.

Why only three references to fasting in the infant stages of church development? The fact that fasting was not mentioned more does not mean fasting was not practiced. The fact that it was specified three times indicates fasting was a practice, not a preoccupation. A preoccupation with fasting can lead to blinding legalism and blinding asceticism. The practice of fasting, however, is one of the benchmarks of a healthy church.

Yet, when was the last time you read a church-health or church-leadership book on the practice of fasting? Chances are you will find more material on fasting in a health-food store than in a Christian bookstore. Could it be that the twenty-first-century church is oblivious to the health-producing practice of Christ-centered, Holy Spirit-anointed, biblically based fasting?

Strictly speaking, fasting simply is abstinence from food. The word *breakfast*, for example, means to break the overnight fast from food. Biblically speaking, fasting is abstinence from food for spiritual, personal, and community reasons.

Biblical fasting focuses on God, bringing the flesh into submission, expressing a hunger for spiritual values over the cravings of the belly.

In *Knowing God Through Fasting*, Dr. Elmer Towns describes the practice of fasting in ten chapter headings:

- *Chapter 1: Emptying.* Fasting is emptying your body of food. In the spiritual realm, it empties you of every barrier to God, so you can be filled with His presence.

- *Chapter 2: Tasting.* Fasting is tasting—creating an appetite for the good things to follow.

- *Chapter 3: Waiting.* Fasting is waiting in God's presence to become like Him and do His purpose.

- *Chapter 4: Coming.* Fasting is coming to the Lord to enjoy His presence and to find spiritual rest.

- *Chapter 5: Drinking.* Fasting is drinking from God's presence in order to get spiritual satisfaction.

- *Chapter 6: Disciplining.* Fasting is disciplining yourself, even as Jesus did.

- *Chapter 7: Growing.* Fasting is growing spiritually into the image of Jesus.

- *Chapter 8: Looking.* Fasting is gaining spiritual perception of God's world.

- *Chapter 9: Resting.* Fasting is more than cessation of activity; it is entering into God's rest.

- *Chapter 10: Knowing.* Fasting is knowing God and becoming more like Him.[1]

There is a woeful lack of the practice of fasting in the consumer-oriented twenty-first-century church. Not only is the practice often neglected, but many do not even know what it is. One little girl, when asked to describe fasting, exclaimed, "Oh, that's easy. Fasting is eating in a hurry!"

I have been blessed. I grew up in a home where biblical fasting was a regular practice. My mother taught me by example both the spiritual and practical value of fasting.

I am humbled by my mother's intimacy with God. I have seen the fruits of her faithfulness. I remember great revivals, spiritual breakthroughs, divine encounters, heaven-sent resources, reaped harvests, healed breaches, turned-around churches, and personal deliverance. To this day she continues to practice fasting and is mightily used of God.

I am blessed to be married to a wonderful and cherished lady who has practiced fasting since high school. As our children grew, time after time I witnessed Peggy going quietly about her duties while fasting. She would tell me one of the kids, our family, or the church was in need or under attack. Then she would say, "I won't be eating for a while."

Without fanfare or complaint, Peggy fasts to "loose the bonds of wickedness, to undo the heavy burdens, to let the oppressed go free, and . . . break every yoke" (Isa. 58:6).

But I cannot shirk my responsibility. I too must practice fasting. I cannot let my mother or my wife excuse me. I must fast. You must fast. For a healthy church and home, we must embrace this biblical practice. In a classic and comprehensive work on fasting, Arthur Wallis says:

> There is concern in the hearts of many for the recovery of apostolic power. But how can we recover apostolic power while neglecting apostolic practice? How can we expect the power to flow if we do not prepare the channels? Fasting is a God-appointed means for the flowing of His grace and power that we can afford to neglect no longer.[2]

Just as fasting can bring health benefits to our physical bodies, it also benefits the Church. A fasting church will be a hungry church . . . hungry for spiritual health and harvest.

6. Partnership With the Holy Spirit Was Embraced

The Holy Spirit said, "Now separate to Me Barnabas and Saul" (Acts 13:2).

How did the church leaders at Antioch know the Holy Spirit had spoken? Simple . . . they were listening! They knew better than to assume their own words were more important than His voice.

A spiritually gifted community of believers, worshiping and fasting, is vital to the health of a church, but this is not enough. The health of a church is not dependent on human investment alone; it is the Holy Spirit who gives life.

The Bible does not reveal the method by which the Holy Spirit spoke to the Antiochian leaders. The Spirit could have spoken through a prophetic word, a word of wisdom, tongues and interpretation, a still small voice, a spirit of unity, even an audible voice. The method of His speaking is His business; listening for His direction is ours.

Listening is not the only connection to our partnership with the Spirit. Sometimes He chooses not to speak. Often He providentially leads us; our responsibility is to follow His leading.

At other times, the Holy Spirit might choose to prevent, forbid, delay, or redirect us. Our task then becomes one of waiting, watching, seeking, discerning. Three principles are essential in partnering with the Holy Spirit.

The Timing Principle

Timing is more important to the Holy Spirit than time. The right action at the wrong time is usually short-lived. The wrong action at the right time usually fails. The right action at the right time is always pleasing to the Holy Spirit. *The birth of Jesus confirmed the timing principle.*

> But when the fullness of time had come, God sent forth His Son, born of a woman (Gal. 4:4).

The life of Jesus confirmed the timing principle. Four times it was said in John's Gospel that Christ's time or hour had not yet come (2:4; 7:6, 30; 8:20). Three times in the same Gospel the confirmation was given that Christ's hour *had* come (12:23; 13:1; 17:1). Timing, not time, is the paramount principle of partnership.

The Testing Principle

Spirit-filled believers enjoy quoting 1 Thessalonians 5:19-20: "Do not quench the Spirit. Do not despise prophecies." We usually stop quoting the passage too soon, however. Verse 21 commands, "Test all things; hold fast what is good." First John 4:1 underscores the testing principle: "Beloved, do not believe every spirit, but test the spirits, whether they are of God."

The Holy Spirit is not quenched or grieved when we seek confirmation of His leadings. The Bible commands us to judge prophecies, tongues, and interpretation of tongues because the spirits of the prophets are subject to the prophets (1 Cor. 14:27-29, 32).

How many times has the health of a church been under attack until it needed intensive care, or maybe life support, because decisions or actions were not tested? Partnership is strengthened by confirmational testing.

If you say, "God told me to do this," you'd better be sure, and you'd better be receptive to the testing principle. Partnership with the Holy Spirit is wounded when we ignore this principle.

I find it interesting that prophecies, tongues, and interpretation of tongues were never used in New Testament times to run the business of the church. These manifestations, which again were to be judged, had as their purposes edification, exhortation, and comfort.

With good reason, the Bible teaches us that "where there is no counsel, the people fall; but in the multitude of counselors there is safety" (Prov. 11:14).

The Holy Spirit is not on trial, our interpretation is. I once bought a car because I felt good and peaceful about it. I mistakenly assumed this was the Holy Spirit's leading. After I bought the car, the front bumper fell off and the windows would not operate properly. It also guzzled gas and burned oil. The car was so bad I had to pay someone to take it off of my hands. The Holy Spirit was *not* my partner; I used Him as my excuse.

The Trusting Principle

The revealed will of the Holy Spirit always requires us to honor the trusting principle. Partnership with the Holy Spirit does not mean we no longer live by faith, walk in courage, endure opposition, or embrace sacrifice.

After Paul's transforming encounter with Jesus on the road to Damascus, the Lord said, "I will show him how many things he must suffer for My name's sake" (Acts 9:16). It is sweet to trust in Jesus . . . but sometimes it is also a struggle.

This is not to say that partnership with the Holy Spirit is all distress, opposition, and sacrifice. It is to say, however, there will be times of questions and discouragement, even to the point of despair (see 2 Cor. 1:8). During these times you must trust your Partner. Once you have satisfied the principle of timing and confirmed the principle of testing, you will be ready to trust . . . and you will!

7. Spiritual Vision Was Pursued

"Separate to Me Barnabas and Saul for the work to which I have called them" (Acts 13:2).

The words "for the work to which I have called them" pulsate with vision. Luke's use of the past tense in the context reveals the fact that both Barnabas and Saul knew specifically what their future looked like. *How* they both knew is interesting.

The New Testament reveals that Paul had four visions during the course of his ministry. The first was near Damascus in AD 37. The second was in Damascus three days later. The third, at Troas, occurred in AD 51. The fourth came to him at Corinth in AD 52. Paul related his first vision in Acts 26. In it he quoted Jesus saying to him:

> I am Jesus, whom you are persecuting. But rise and stand on your feet; for I have appeared to you for this purpose, to make you a minister and a witness both of the things which you have seen and of the things which I will yet reveal to you. I will deliver you from the Jewish people, as well as from the Gentiles, to whom I now send you, to open their eyes, in order to turn them from darkness to light, and from the power of Satan to God, that they may receive forgiveness of sins and an inheritance among those who are sanctified by faith in Me (vv. 15-18).

Paul added, "I was not disobedient to the heavenly vision" (v. 19).

Barnabas' story is different. There is no record that Barnabas ever saw a vision. How could he know his future without a personal vision? The answer: *Barnabas was called to share the vision Christ had given Paul.*

Study the lives of Silas and Timothy. There is no record that they ever saw a vision. They were chosen by the Lord to be partners in the vision Christ gave to Paul.

It is easy to miss the big principle: *You don't have to see a vision to have vision.* If you have not *seen* a vision, perhaps the Lord is calling you to *share* in a vision He has given someone else. A vision is always bigger than a single person. One may get the picture, but many are needed to develop it.

A healthy church has a single vision. An unhealthy church with more than one vision has "di-vision."

8. SPIRITUAL AUTHORITY WAS RESPECTED

"Separate to Me Barnabas and Saul" (Acts 13:2).

Because Christ is the head of the Church, the Holy Spirit engenders respect for spiritual authority. But what is spiritual authority?

Spiritual authority is the delegated influence of God through which Christ leads the Church by the Holy Spirit. True spiritual authority is not about manipulation, domination, or absorption. It is about cooperation with the Head of the Church, who is the delegator of His influence. Why is spiritual authority essential? Because it . . .

- Promotes personal growth (Luke 2:51-52)

- Provides corporate protection (10:19-20)

- Prioritizes social order (Rom. 13:1-7)

- Prefaces great faith (Luke 7: 8-9).

How is spiritual authority delegated? It is discerned, learned, earned, and concerned. Many believers think there are only two attitudes that can be demonstrated toward spiritual authority. The Bible reveals three. We can . . .

- Respect and respond

- Reject and rebel

- React and resign.

Perhaps this is why the Holy Spirit chose to give us the story of Barnabas and Saul.

In the local-church context at Antioch, Barnabas was the responsible and recognized spiritual authority over Saul. This responsibility shifted to Saul (Paul), however, soon after these two men began their first missionary journey (Acts 13:13).

There is no indication Barnabas had a problem with this role reversal. For five years, AD 45-50, the two men traveled, preached, planted churches, suffered, and sacrificed as a team. So far, so good, but an interesting thing happened on the way to their second endeavor. As they planned their second tour of ministry, sharp contention arose between them.

Barnabas was determined that John Mark, his young cousin, would accompany them on the journey. Paul was equally resolute that the young man, who had left the team five years earlier to return home, would not go. Paul's thinking might have been:

Missionary work is dangerous and stressful. It requires a deep level of commitment. We don't have the luxury of taking an upstart who has already proven he can't take the heat. Besides, a relative will require too much diversion of Barnabas' energy and attention. We have enough problems without taking another with us. No, John Mark can't go!

On the other hand, Barnabas' thoughts might have been:

Give me a break, Paul! You are really someone to be judgmental. Remember where you were when I found you? I gave you the same encouragement I want to give to John Mark. The boy has a lot to offer. We have to give him a second chance. Besides, it has been five years since his mistake. How is he ever going to learn if we don't teach him?

With twenty centuries of perspective, we can see that both were right. Scripture doesn't say that either prayed for direction or that the Holy Spirit volunteered a solution. Does this story sound familiar?

At this point, Paul was the responsible spiritual authority. Barnabas could respect and respond, reject and rebel, or react and resign. Barnabas took John Mark and went home to Cyprus (Acts 15:39). It appears Barnabas took the third option.

Five years earlier, in Antioch, Barnabas had been called by the Holy Spirit and commissioned by spiritual authorities (elders). He was under spiritual authority. Five years later, because he disagreed with Paul, Barnabas reacted and resigned.

Choices have consequences. Barnabas vanished from the Spirit-inspired pages of Acts. He is mentioned only five more times in the New Testament: three times in Galatians 2, and once each in 1 Corinthians 9 and Colossians 4. While Galatians was written two years before the dispute, the other references are sidelights to Barnabas' personal life. Sadly, his missionary ministry was over.

What happened to Mark? Barnabas continued to be a positive influence and the young man *was* worth a second chance. Paul's severity probably helped develop Mark's character, too. Eventually, Paul's fellowship with Mark was restored (Col. 4:10). Just before his death, Paul wrote to Timothy: "Get Mark and bring him with you, for he is useful to me for ministry" (2 Tim. 4:11).

What happened to Barnabas—first pastor at Antioch, the man who was Paul's mentor and partner, the "good man" full of the Holy Spirit and faith? We don't know for sure. Your guess is probably better than mine. But there is a principle unveiled in this story.

Where there are no biblical or moral breaches, it is best to respect and respond to spiritual authority. Sometimes we might not agree with decisions. And yes, it is okay to ask questions and seek answers.

When there are no clear answers, however, it is better to respect and respond. When we react and resign, we weaken the health of the Church. It is far more advantageous to give the Holy Spirit time to work out the details. Healthy churches live by this principle.

9. A Divine Calling Clarified Ministry

"Separate to Me Barnabas and Saul for the work to which I have called them" (Acts 13:2).

Every believer has one. Some never realize it. It is larger than life, but must be lived out daily. It is personally given, publicly demonstrated. It actualizes God's will, yet depends on individual willingness. It lasts a lifetime, but can be rejected in a moment. It requires sacrifice, but leads to fulfillment. It can be given to the inexperienced and immature, but requires involvement and personal growth. It is indestructible, yet must be handled with care.

What is it? *It is the individual, personalized call of God.* It is the revelation of God expressing His unique purpose for your life. Some discern their calling over a period of time. Others may get a revelation in an unforgettable instant. Either way, the call is the clarifier. If they did not know before, the leaders at Antioch quickly realized that the call of God given by the Holy Spirit is a necessity. The Word of God is clear on the matter of calling. Paul wrote to Timothy:

> [God] has saved us and called us with a holy calling, not according to our works, but according to His own purpose and grace which was given to us in Christ Jesus before time began (2 Tim. 1:9).

Many people are confused over the subject of calling because they miss the fact that there are two dimensions to the call of God. *First*, every believer is called (1 Cor. 7:17). This is the universal calling:

- We are called to be saints (Rom. 1:7).
- We are called into active fellowship with Christ (1 Cor. 1:9).
- We are called to peace (7:15).
- We are called to grace (Gal. 1:6).
- We are called to liberty (5:13).
- We are called to hope (Eph. 1:18).
- We are called to holiness (1 Thess. 4:7).
- We are called into one body (Col. 3:15).
- We are called to suffer patiently (1 Peter 2:21).

Second, there is a personalized, specific calling. This is the individual calling:

- We were separated from our mother's womb and called through God's grace (Gal. 1:15).
- We are gloriously called in one hope of our calling (Eph. 4:4).
- We are His workmanship, created in Christ Jesus for good works, which God prepared before we were born (2:10).
- We are to walk worthy of the calling to which we are called (4:1).
- We are to remain in the same calling to which we were called (1 Cor. 7:20).
- Faithfulness will result in God's enablement to accomplish our particular calling (1 Tim. 1:12).
- We should recognize our individual calling because both the gifts and calling of God are irrevocable (Rom. 11:29).

The call of God is not fully realized until we actualize both the universal and individual callings in our lives. Some people answer the call like Barnabas and Saul, who were called to pastoral, missionary, and itinerant roles.

Others are called to serve within a specific community of believers—like Simeon, Lucius, and Manaen. The Simeons of the Church are no less important than the Barnabases.

Vocation and calling are not the same. Your calling is not validated by who pays your salary; your calling is the result of the Savior who canceled your debt. What you do for a living only *supports* what you do with your life. It is your life that counts.

> *Abraham* was a herdsman.
>
> *Daniel* was in government.
>
> *Ruth* was a field hand.
>
> *Nehemiah* was in civil service.
>
> *Amos* was a cattleman who grew fruit.
>
> *Mary* was a housewife.
>
> *Peter* was in seafood.
>
> *Philip* was a businessman.
>
> *Lydia* was a tailor.
>
> *Paul* was in tent-making.

Thank God, they all fulfilled their purpose, responded to their calling, and bloomed where they were planted. Calling was, and is, the supreme clarifier. For the Church, calling is a health principle. Healthy, vibrant churches develop when the Holy Spirit is regularly calling believers into specific areas of ministry.

I admit that, at first, it wasn't easy for me to accept calling as the clarifier. As a young, inexperienced pastor I would preach, "Everyone is called into ministry." Then, I would feel insecure, even threatened, when people accepted individualized callings that required me to take risks and clean up messes.

I sincerely wanted people to be called, but was subconsciously reluctant to give up control of ministry to the Holy Spirit. I had to learn some hard lessons. There's a difference between controlling and leading, competing and completing, directing and developing, my work and teamwork.

It is a shame that I had to repeat the grade so many times before I learned the lessons. God calls people to do things other than to preach or pastor. If I can trust the wisdom of God in His calling for my life, I should trust Him to take care of His church when I relinquish control of ministry to the Holy Spirit. After all, it is not my church, it is His church.

Does this talk of calling mean that doctrine, discipline, structure, training, and personal growth are of minimal importance? No! A thousand times no!

Once we are called, we are commanded to learn, to grow, to develop. Peter says it best:

> [God has] called us by glory and virtue. . . . Giving all diligence, add to your faith virtue, to virtue knowledge, to knowledge self-control, to self-control perseverance, to perseverance godliness, to godliness brotherly kindness, and to brotherly kindness love. For if these things are yours and abound, you will be neither barren nor unfruitful in the knowledge of our Lord Jesus Christ (2 Peter 1:2-8).

Healthy churches know that divine calling clarifies ministry. Personal training, discipline, and growth expand ministry.

10. MISSIONAL LEADERSHIP WAS PRACTICED

Then, having fasted and prayed, and laid hands on them, they sent them away (Acts 13:3).

The church's leaders at Antioch were on a mission from God. Barnabas and Paul had been called by the Holy Spirit, but it was the local leaders who had the responsibility to commission them. Meet Antioch's missional leaders:

- Simeon
- Lucius
- Manaen

Some read this story and mistakenly assume it is a snapshot of the *senders* and the *sent*. Wrong! All five leaders, including Barnabas and Paul, were both *sent* and *senders*. Is this just semantics? Hardly. The local leaders at Antioch were as called, anointed, and purpose-focused as the two we call "missionaries."

The truth is, they were all sent by the Holy Spirit. Each was fulfilling a role as a missional leader. Each was a missionary because each was fulfilling a divine mission. Separating the *sender* from the *sent* has cost the North American church much in terms of laborers for the harvest.

Many people view missionaries (the traditionally viewed *sent*) as those who do ministry overseas or in a foreign country. This perspective leads us to assume that evangelism is what we do in North America while missions is what people do on other continents.

Population statistics reveal that the third-largest mission field in the world is North America. The Church, then, is God's missionary to North America as much as to any country overseas.

Dr. Tom Clegg is a missionary called *to* America *from* Africa. He has coauthored a book with Warren Bird titled *Lost in America*. In an interview in *Today's Pentecostal Evangel*, Clegg makes these observations:

> To be a missionary in Africa was everything I dreamed of and more. I loved it. When it was clear I was returning to America, I came back with great reluctance. Compared to the African savanna, ministry in America is much harder. In Africa, there might be germs in the water, bandits with guns, or even animals that could harm you, but none of those dangers compare with the apathy and indifference you find in America.

Clegg went on to point out why he views America as a mission field:

- The country with the largest Christian church in the world is not America, but South Korea.
- The world's second-largest Christian church is not in America, it is in Lagos, Nigeria.
- The world's largest Buddhist temple is in America—Boulder, Colorado.
- The world's largest Muslim training center is in America—New York City.

- The world's largest training center for transcendental meditation is in America—Fairfield, Ohio.

- The country with the largest Jewish population is the United States, not Israel.

- The ethnic group in North America most responsive to the Gospel is Asian Americans.

- Despite our Christian heritage, the United States leads the industrial world in the percentage of single-parent families, abortion rates, sexually transmitted diseases, teenage birthrates, use of illegal drugs by students, and prison population.

- Only 40 percent of American adults said they went to church last week. That's down from 42 percent in 1995 and 49 percent in 1991.

- Approximately half of all churches in America did not add a single new person through conversion last year.[3]

Sadly, dropouts from American Christianity are escalating:

- The nonreligious have grown from a million in 1900 to twenty-six million today.

- The Muslim population in the U.S. grew by 25 percent between 1989 and 1998.

- Buddhism in America is growing three times as fast as Christianity.

- Hinduism is the second fastest-growing religion in the U.S.[3]

The website *www.ethnicharvest.org* reports that while the general population of the U.S. grew by 6 percent in the

1990s, the number of Asians grew by 107 percent, Hispanics grew by 53 percent, and the number of Native Americans grew by 38 percent.

Dorothy said it best in *The Wizard of Oz*: "We are not in Kansas anymore." Yesterday's church was the *sender*. Today's church must become both the *sender* and the *sent*. The harvest is not before us, it is among us! We're past due for changing our perspective but not too late if we are willing to lead with a missional mind-set.

Missional leadership is built squarely on mission. It is more than having a mission statement in print; it is having a mission in people. It is both becoming "all things to all men, that I might by all means save some" (1 Cor. 9:22) and contending "earnestly for the faith which was once for all delivered to the saints" (Jude 3). From the words of Jesus, we learn that missional leadership rests on four pillars:

> 1. The *Method*—"As the Father has sent Me, I also send you" (John 20:21).
>
> 2. The *Message*—"It was necessary . . . that repentance and remission of sins should be preached in His name to all nations, beginning at Jerusalem" (Luke 24:46-47).
>
> 3. The *Mission*—"Go therefore and make disciples of all the nations, baptizing them . . . teaching them to observe all things that I have commanded you" (Matt. 28:19-20).
>
> 4. The *Means*—"But you shall receive power when the Holy Spirit has come upon you; and you shall be witnesses to Me in Jerusalem, and in all Judea and Samaria, and to the end of the earth" (Acts 1:8).

Missional leadership—different from corporate, governmental, and sports leadership—is spiritual leadership. It doesn't lead for profit, politics, or the applause of man. It leads for the greatest Missionary who ever walked on earth—Jesus Christ. It leads the greatest mission ever undertaken—the mission of the Church.

The starting point of leadership is not actions, but assumptions. What we assume about leadership usually defines the way we lead. Look at some of the false assumptions we make about missional leadership.

Ten Myths About Missional Leadership

1. *My position makes me the leader.* Position merely opens the door. Effective leadership keeps us in the room. Titles are easy to come by. True leaders . . . well, that's another story.

2. *If I do this, I'll get that.* Many get discouraged because what looked good on paper, sounded great in a meeting, or worked at some other church does not work for them. Like missionaries, missional leaders take time to learn about the culture and context in the community where they minister. What works in San Diego may not work in Selma. Building a new sanctuary, dressing "down" in jeans and a T-shirt, and disbanding the choir might work *for* you, but know that it can work *against* you.

3. *I'm the leader . . . I'm the boss.* Spiritual authority must be delegated by God, developed by the leader, and accepted by the people. It takes time—a long time. True spiritual authority is not about being boss, it has more to do with being responsible.

4. *I'm the leader . . . I can change things.* True. If you change too much too fast, the biggest change you'll face is when the people change the leader—you!

5. *I don't have to explain myself to anyone.* When leaders can explain *why* a certain decision or direction is being taken—not just *what* the decision is—they provide a reasonable rationale for change. Spend hours in prayer and thoughtful meditation, with a notepad, to develop a rationale. If you can't explain it, "can" it. If you can't explain it and *don't* "can" it, the people will!

6. *I'm more important than the people I lead.* You are more strategic because you are the leader. But you are *never, never* more important.

7. *I'm smarter, more spiritual, and more mature than the people I lead.* Leadership doesn't boost your IQ, bring you closer to God, or neutralize immaturity. It simply provides the opportunity to serve God and the church.

8. *I must keep up my image.* The one image most important to a missional leader is Christ's image. Do you reflect it? Do you reproduce it?

9. *All I need is vision and I'll be a great leader.* The question is, What is the source of your vision? In the excellent book *Spiritual Leadership*, Henry and Richard Blackaby cite various sources from which people get vision. While reading this inspirational volume, these words leaped off of page 69:

The previous [various] sources of vision have one thing in common—they are all generated by worldly thinking. This is not surprising; *the world functions by vision*. But God does not ask His people to operate by vision. God's people live by revelation.

Proverbs 29:18, although widely used, is also widely misapplied. The popular translation is, "Where there is no vision, the people perish" (KJV). A more accurate translation of the Hebrew is: "Where there is no revelation, the people cast off restraint."

There is a significant difference between revelation and vision. Vision is something people produce; revelation is something people receive. Leaders can dream up a vision, but they cannot unilaterally get a revelation. God must reveal it.

The secular world ignores God's will, so nonbelievers are left with one alternative—to project their own vision. Christians are called to a totally different approach. For Christians, God sets the agenda.[4]

10.   *Failure is not an option.* Sure it is! Basketball star Michael Jordan missed more than 9,000 shots in his career, and lost 300 games. Twenty-six times he was trusted to take the winning shot, and missed! "I've failed over and over in my life. And that's why I succeed." It doesn't matter if you try and fail; it only matters if you try and fail . . . and fail to try again!"

Missional leaders don't have to be perfect to be effective. When they fail, they learn from failure and keep on growing. Leadership is about learning, and learning takes a lifetime.

What Can You Do?

Perhaps the Holy Spirit is urging you to be more missional in your leadership by transforming your church into a missionary to your town. Perhaps you need to wake up your church to the realities of your mission field, America. Perhaps you are weary of focusing on the barn and are ready to move into the harvest. What can you do? In *Breaking the Missional Code: Your Church Can Become a Missionary in Your Community*, Ed Stetzer and David Putman list five simple steps.

1. *Confirm your calling from God.* Our first task is to listen for God's call to us, not to respond to His call to others. Many church planters, pastors, and various leaders simply seize the first "cool" model that comes along and attempt to make it fit into their communities. Ask, "Who are You calling me to reach?"

2. *Exegete your community.* Seek to understand your culture. As you decipher your own community, you may discover methods that have been used effectively in other like-minded communities.

3. *See how God is working in similar communities.*

4. *Find God's unique vision (revelation) for your church.* When it comes to the kingdom of God, uniformity is not a value. Instead, Scripture speaks of diversity and celebrates every tongue, tribe, and nation. God is most glorified when the churches that honor Him reflect the diversity of His vast kingdom. Thus, every church must find its unique call and vision.

5. *Adjust the vision as you learn the context.* If a church does not regularly examine its culture, it ends up as a culture to itself, relating to issues that were relevant 100 years before. Instead, the church needs to regularly ask, "Are we faithfully proclaiming the faith in the place in which we find ourselves today?[5]

Healthy churches demonstrate spiritual leadership, promote personal stewardship, nurture community, offer God-centered worship, practice fasting, embrace partnership with the Holy Spirit, pursue spiritual vision, respect spiritual authority, clarify calling in ministry, and practice missional leadership.

Churches that do this won't be left behind.

Meditating on the Message

1. Of the ten identifying marks of a healthy church, which ones are most evident in your local church?

2. How do *isolation*, *insulation*, and *incubation* affect community in a church?

3. How do the three principles for confirming partnership with the Holy Spirit impact a church's passion for outreach?

Assignment: Think of some ways your church can employ the action principles given on pages 169 and 170.

Chapter 8

Prayer—the Heartbeat of a Healthy Church

Prayer is not a characteristic of health, it is the very character of health. Prayer is the rhythmic and perpetual heartbeat of the body of Christ. It sustains and energizes the Church, providing fervency for worship, strength and energy for serving, and motivation for action. It is an indispensable lifeline to the resources of heaven.

> As they ministered to the Lord and fasted, the Holy Spirit said, "Now separate to Me Barnabas and Saul for the work to which I have called them." Then, having fasted and prayed, and laid hands on them, they sent them away (Acts 13:2-3).

In his book, *Leadership That Works*, Dr. Leith Anderson recounts the true story of a denomination that found itself in serious decline. The denominational leaders called on a church-consulting firm to assess the problem and prescribe a cure.

After months of study, research, and interviews, the consultants met with church leaders. The denomination was told it was too far gone. Nothing substantive could be done to reverse the decline.

Sitting in stunned silence, the leaders were motionless. Finally, one leader broke the silence to ask, "Are you telling us there is *nothing* we can do?"

"Well," came the response, "you can pray."

With that verdict, the leader turned, fell to his knees, and began to pray. Together, the leaders prayed through their lunch hour and into the afternoon. They began meeting regularly to pray. They called their people to prayer. God heard their prayers, arrested the decline, and today that group is moving forward.[1]

Prayer must be our most strategic action if we are to have spiritual renewal. History proves the power of prayer. Dr. Charles W. Conn references prayer, seeking God, and supplication at least forty-three times in his first five chapters of Church of God history, *Like a Mighty Army*. We read comments like these:

- They spent much time in prayer, praying into the night.
- They were praying and weeping constantly.

No Church Left Behind

- They were given much to prayer and fasting.
- They sang, gave testimonies, and prayed. The important thing is, they prayed.
- Because revival was resisted in existing churches, the few who ardently desired it banded themselves together and prayed—and God heard their supplication.[2]

Other historical accounts, like the General Assembly *Minutes* and the *Church of God Evangel*, tell a similar story. The first General Assembly of 1906 left this record: "It is therefore the sense of this assembly that we recommend, advise and urge that each local church hold a prayer meeting at least once a week."[3] Headlines in the *Church of God Evangel* in the early 1920s often prompted the church to join "in great days of prayer."

Our Pentecostal roots grow deeply into the soil of prayer. Prayer stabilized us in our infancy. Prayer gave victory in the face of persecution. Prayer sustained balance amid fanaticism. Prayer strengthened us through decades of cultural change and satanic attacks.

Prayer is the heartbeat of the Church. This is why the Bible enjoins us to . . .

- "Seek the Lord and His strength; seek His face evermore" (1 Chron. 16:11)!
- "Ask . . . seek . . . knock" (Matt. 7:7).
- "Watch therefore, and pray always" (Luke 21:36).
- "[Pray] always with all prayer and supplication in the Spirit . . . for all the saints" (Eph. 6:18).

- "Continue earnestly in prayer, being vigilant" (Col. 4:2).
- "Pray without ceasing" (1 Thess. 5:17).
- "The harvest truly is plentiful, but the laborers are few. Therefore pray the Lord of the harvest to send out laborers into His harvest" (Matt. 9:37-38).

The harvest *is* plentiful! Experts tell us more people are alive today than have ever lived in history combined. God has decided the death of His Son will not have been in vain. Spirit-ignited revival fires burning around the world are fanned by the winds of prayer.

The church at Antioch was praying and fasting when God spoke to them. What were they praying for?

People fast and pray when they are grieving over the death of a loved one (2 Sam. 12:16). People fast and pray when they repent of the sins of the nation (Dan. 9:3). Most often, however, people fast and pray when they are seeking God's will for their lives, their church, or their nation (Neh. 1:4).

Perhaps we are not told what Antioch's leaders were praying for because the simple fact is, they had no idea what God had in mind for them. They only knew God had something for them and they had not realized it yet.

John Maxwell said, "Our prayers should ask God to help us do what He is blessing, not bless what we are doing." Rather than make our own agenda and ask God to bless it, why not pray for insight into His agenda for the Church and get on the same page with Him?

No Church Left Behind

Watchman Nee said, "Prayer is not just asking God for something. For the Church to pray means it stands on God's side to declare that man wants what God wants." When the Antiochian leaders made themselves available for anything God had in store for them, two of them were divinely called to a special ministry that will impact the Church until Jesus comes.

Prayer is the holy and intimate intersection of God and His church, where He delegates authority to His church to enforce His will on earth as it is in heaven.

Prayer is more than presentation; it is partnership. It is more than exercise; it is enforcement. It is more than activity; it is authority. Prayer is our mission because praying is our ministry. Whatever we may or may not do, we must stay on our knees. The Church has made giant strides forward in the last century, but we did it on our knees.

If we are to evangelize, plant churches, disciple believers, raise up leaders, and preach the Gospel, we must pray. Let us teach prayer. Let us preach prayer. Most of all, let us pray. Our mission is our ministry. As we pray, we will prevail.

PRAYER IS INTERACTION

Prayer is, first and foremost, interaction with God. Revelation 5:8 describes a scene in heaven where "twenty-four elders fell down before the Lamb, each having a harp, and golden bowls full of incense, which are the prayers of the saints."

In chapter 8, "the smoke of the incense, with the prayers of the saints, ascended before God" (v. 4). Prayer is the sacred, aromatic perfume of heaven that interacts without interruption with the eternal God.

But interaction with those around us is also involved in our praying. If prayer is not being answered, here are *six circuit-breakers to answered prayer.*

1. Fractured Relationships With Others

> You husbands must give honor to your wives. Treat your wife with understanding as you live together. She may be weaker than you are, but she is your equal partner in God's gift of new life. Treat her as you should so your prayers will not be hindered (1 Peter 3:7 NLT).

These instructions, addressed specifically to husbands, are equally applicable to wives. Verbal abuse, psychological battering, and perpetual put-downs are alien intrusions in a Christian home. When a husband and wife fight like cats and dogs, it is important to remember that God doesn't hear prayers from a dog-and-cat fight.

We should check our relationship with our spouse as well as with others whom God has put in our lives. The key to unanswered prayers is often found in our relations with one another. Abused relationships are circuit-breakers. How we treat others matters to the Master. Unhealthy, fractured, or completely severed relationships affect our praying.

2. Wrong Motives in Prayer

> You ask and do not receive, because you ask amiss,
> that you may spend it on your pleasures (James 4:3).

A prayer can be proper and according to the will of God, but prayed from the wrong motive.

- Are we praying to build a name for *ourselves*, or to glorify *God* and advance His *kingdom*?

- Do we want Kingdom growth so it will lift *us* up, or to lift *Him* up?

- Do we want growth so it will make *us look good* in the community and with our peers, or are we praying *to see His kingdom coming*?

- Do we want revival so *we can feel good*, or so *people will be empowered* and inspired to win the lost to Jesus in the community?

- Do we want *our subculture enhanced*, or *the lost saved*?

Let's check our motives.

3. Hidden or Deliberate Sin

> The Lord's hand is not shortened, that it cannot save;
> nor His ear heavy, that it cannot hear. But your
> iniquities have separated you from your God; and
> your sins have hidden His face from you, so that He
> will not hear (Isa. 59:1-2).

At a young age Norman Vincent Peale decided to sneak around and smoke, contrary to his minister-father's instructions. He bought a large, black cigar and began puffing on it as he meandered down a side street. Suddenly he saw, only a half-block away, his father coming straight toward him. When they met, the guilty boy kept the forbidden cigar behind his back as he tried desperately to find something to say.

Finally, he made a halfhearted request of his father. Peale said his father's answer was not harsh but it was firm: "Norman, one of the first lessons you should learn is to never make a petition while trying to hide a smoldering disobedience behind your back."

Unconfessed sin in the heart breaks the power connection with God. It may be a past transgression that is unconfessed and "un-judged," it may be a cherished present sin we do not think of as sin, or it may be a "smoldering disobedience." But sin in the heart, whether deliberate or hidden, slams the door to God's storehouse of blessings. David prayed:

> Search me [thoroughly], O God, and know my heart! Try me and know my thoughts! And see if there is any wicked or hurtful way in me, and lead me in the way everlasting (Ps. 139:23-24 Amp.).

David's prayer for forgiveness for hidden sin in Psalm 51 is well known. Less known, however, is his prayer of praise and triumph after the sin had been forgiven:

Come and hear, all you who fear God, and I will declare what He has done for my soul. I cried to Him with my mouth, and He was extolled with my tongue. If I regard iniquity in my heart, the Lord will not hear. But certainly God has heard me; He has attended to the voice of my prayer. Blessed be God, who has not turned away my prayer, nor His mercy from me! (66:16-20).

4. Overlooked Idols

Idols? Us? In our hearts?

> "Son of man, these leaders have set up idols in their hearts. They have embraced things that will make them fall into sin. Why should I listen to their requests?" (Ezek. 14:3 NLT).

Samson never had a haircut until late in his life. In childhood he was dedicated as a Nazirite, and his parents were zealous in their obedience to the Lord. As a young adult, he continued that obedience and the Spirit of God would move on him. He began doing great exploits and it became obvious that there was something unusual about Samson (Judg. 13:25).

At various times Samson displayed almost unbelievable physical strength, and that strength became legendary. He was the superhero of ancient Israel. On one occasion, Samson killed a lion with his bare hands (14:6). At another time, the Lord used him to defeat thirty Philistines single-handedly (v. 19). Once he defeated a thousand of the enemy without help from anyone (15:14-15).

Called by God and respected by the people, Samson became the last and most famous judge of Israel. He served twenty years in this capacity (16:31). Over time, he came to take great pride in his personal appearance and handsome looks. His long, luxurious hair became an idol in his heart. Samson began believing his strength was in his "seven locks of hair" (see v. 13), when in fact his strength was in his obedience to and anointing by God.

Idols in the heart neutralize God's anointing in even the best of people. Eventually God's mighty judge and deliverer lost his anointing and his strength. What a sad day it was when Samson went out and did not know the Lord had departed from him (v. 20)!

Today, idols of the heart may include good looks, popularity, business acumen, accumulated wealth, a hard-earned education, a well-polished image, even seniority in the Kingdom. An idol is anything that takes the place of God, anything that is the supreme object of our affection. Some have even made the church an idol.

God asks, "Why should I listen to your requests when cherished idols block the path of prayer?"

5. Neglect of Forgiveness

Unforgiveness is a major circuit-breaker. Refusing to forgive is one of the most common hindrances to prayer. An unforgiving spirit will short-circuit the power of prayer every time. Jesus said in Mark 11:25-26:

Whenever you stand praying, if you have anything against anyone, forgive him, that your Father in heaven may also forgive you your trespasses. But if you do not forgive, neither will your Father in heaven forgive your trespasses.

God answers the prayers of the Church based on the fact our sins are forgiven. How can He deal with us on the basis of forgiveness if we have ill will against those who have wronged us? We must forgive others if we expect God to forgive us.

Every one of us has to forgive whoever has wronged us at any time. How tragic it is to allow secret grudges to fester in our hearts because someone once wronged or injured us. Freely we have received forgiveness; freely we must give forgiveness to others.

6. An Unyielding Heart

About 500 years before Christ, the prophet Zechariah recorded these words from the Lord:

"They refused to heed, shrugged their shoulders, and stopped their ears so that they could not hear. Yes, they made their hearts like flint, refusing to hear the law and the words which the Lord of hosts had sent by His Spirit through the former prophets. Thus great wrath came. . . . Therefore it happened, that just as He proclaimed and they would not hear, so they called out and I would not listen," says the Lord (7:11-13).

Because they shrugged their shoulders and put their fingers in their ears to keep from hearing the message God sent through His Spirit, their hearts became hard and they brought the wrath of God down on themselves. If we want God to listen to us when we pray, we have to listen to Him when He speaks to us.

Prayer Is Intercession

The difference in the Old and New Testament ministry of priests and the priesthood is explained in Hebrews 7:11-19. The Levitical priesthood of the Old Testament was passed down from generation to generation through the descendants of the tribe of Levi.

In the New Testament, a new order of the priesthood emerged—the priesthood of the believers. Like Melchisedek, these new priests do not inherit their right to be priests from, or receive it by, the Law. They are appointed priests by God.

This priesthood of believers is passed on to all believers through Christ's blood when we experience the new birth. Jesus himself is the "High Priest" (8:1; 9:11). Peter wrote that we are a "holy priesthood" (1 Peter 2:5) and a "royal priesthood (v. 9).

Together, all believers form a kingdom of priests. This imposes on each of us a solemn and sacred responsibility to pray. We must intercede for ourselves and our own needs, to be sure, but as priests of God we must intercede for others. In fact, interceding is what the Head of the church is doing now:

No Church Left Behind

He is also able to save to the uttermost those who come to God through Him, since He always lives to make intercession for them (Heb. 7:25).

To Him who loved us and washed us from our sins in His own blood, and has made us kings and priests to His God and Father, to Him be glory and dominion forever and ever. Amen (Rev. 1:5-6).

- Intercessory prayer helps to save the lives of church leaders.

Herod . . . killed James the brother of John with the sword. And because he saw that it pleased the Jews, he proceeded further to seize Peter also. . . . Peter was therefore kept in prison, but constant prayer was offered to God for him by the church. The Lord . . . brought him out of the prison (Acts 12:1-3, 5, 17).

- Intercessory prayer brings healing.

Pray for one another, that you may be healed (James 5:16).

- Intercessory prayer restores morality and reverence, giving society stability and peace.

I exhort . . . that supplications, prayers, intercessions, and giving of thanks be made for all men, for kings and all who are in authority, that we may lead a quiet and peaceable life in all godliness and reverence (1 Tim. 2:1-2).

- Intercessory prayer keeps our friends in times of trial and temptation.

"Simon! Indeed, Satan has asked for you, that he may sift you as wheat. But I have prayed for you, that your faith should not fail" (Luke 22:31-32).

- Intercessory prayer opens closed doors.

  Pray for us, too, that God may open a door for our message, so that we may proclaim the mystery of Christ (Col. 4:3 NIV).

- Intercessory prayer opens up truth to us in an understandable way.

  I bow my knees to the Father of our Lord Jesus Christ . . . that He would grant you . . . to be strengthened with might through His Spirit . . . that Christ may dwell in your hearts through faith; that you . . . may be able to comprehend with all the saints what is the width and length and depth and height—to know the love of Christ which passes knowledge; that you may be filled with all the fullness of God (Eph. 3:14-19).

- Intercessory prayer helps believers to grow spiritually.

  I pray for you constantly, asking God, the glorious Father of our Lord Jesus Christ, to give you spiritual wisdom and insight so that you might grow in your knowledge of God (1:16-18 NLT).

PRAYER IS INTERSECTION

Prayer is the intersection between God and man, the junction where we meet with the Almighty, the crossroads where our needs and God's providence come together, the entrance ramp to God's flow of endless blessings, the exit ramp of life, where we pause on the journey to acquire spiritual refreshing.

What is prayer? It is *relationship with God* (John 15:5, 7). Prayer is *fellowship with God* (1 Cor. 1:9). Prayer is also *partnership with God* (Matt. 26:36-37). Healthy churches are praying churches! When we pray . . .

- We walk in the footsteps of Jesus, who told Peter, "I have prayed for you, that your faith should not fail" (Luke 22:32).

- We lift up the example of Paul, who wrote: "We give thanks to the God and Father of our Lord Jesus Christ, praying always for you" (Col. 1:3).

- We follow the pattern of Moses, who interceded with God for people who had sinned (Ex. 32:31-32).

- We fulfill our biblical responsibility to "pray for one another" (James 5:16).

- We exercise our faith in Jesus' promise: "Whatever things you ask when you pray, believe that you receive them, and you will have them" (Mark 11:24).

- We affirm that Christ has given us fruit, for Jesus said, "I chose you and appointed you . . . [to] bear fruit, and that your fruit should remain, that whatever you ask the Father in My name He may give you" (John 15:16).

- We lift loads from others and assure joy for ourselves, for Paul wrote: "Bear one another's burdens, and so fulfill the law of Christ. . . . Let each one examine his own work [in prayer], and then he will have rejoicing" (Gal. 6:2, 4).

- We resist the sin of prayerlessness, for God's Word says in 1 Samuel 12:23: "Far be it from me that I should sin against the Lord in ceasing to pray for you."

PRAYER IS INTIMACY

A man's daughter asked the minister to come and pray with her father. The minister found the man lying in bed with his head propped up on two pillows. An empty chair sat beside his bed. The pastor assumed that the old fellow had been informed of his visit.

"I guess you were expecting me," he said. "No, who are you?" said the father.

The minister told him his name, and said, "I see the empty chair. I figured you knew I was going to show up."

"Oh yeah, the chair," said the bedridden man. "Would you mind closing the door?" Puzzled, the minister shut the door.

"I have never told anyone this, not even my daughter," said the man. "But all of my life I have never known how to pray. At church I used to hear the pastor talk about prayer, but it went right over my head. I abandoned any attempt at prayer."

The old man continued: "Four years ago, my best friend said to me, 'Johnny, prayer is just a simple matter of having a conversation with Jesus. Here is what I suggest: Sit down in a chair, place an empty chair in front of you, and in faith see Jesus on the chair. It's not spooky because He promised, "I'll be with you always." Then just speak to Him in the same way you're doing with me right now.'"

"So, I tried it and I've liked it so much that I do it a couple of hours every day. I'm careful though. If my daughter saw me talking to an empty chair, she'd have a nervous breakdown or send me off to the funny farm."

The minister was deeply moved by the story and encouraged the old man to continue on the journey. Then he prayed with him, anointed him with oil, and returned to the church.

Two nights later the daughter called to tell the minister that her daddy had died that afternoon.

"Did he die in peace?" he asked.

"Yes, when I left the house about two o'clock, he called me over to his bedside, told me he loved me and kissed me on the cheek. When I got back from the store an hour later, I found him dead. But there was something strange about his death. Apparently, just before Daddy died, he leaned over and rested his head on the chair beside the bed. What do you make of that?"

The minister wiped a tear from his eye and said, "I wish we could all go like that."

John Wesley said, "The purpose of your praying is not to inform God, as though He didn't already know what you wanted. It is to inform yourself, to fix your wants more clearly in your heart and to remind yourself of your continual dependence on God, who is always more willing to give than you are to ask."

Let me challenge you with this final thought: Can you dream big enough to match the plans God has for your church? I heard of a man who had been asking God in prayer to bless his plans, but he didn't seem to be getting an answer. One night he dreamed he saw the Lord. He asked the Lord why he wasn't getting any answer. The Lord kindly replied, "No bigger than your plans are, you don't need My help! I answer the prayer of those with plans too big to do the job themselves."

Look at what happened when the Antioch leaders fasted and prayed for the health of the church:

The Holy Spirit called Barnabas and Paul to a special ministry.

The church set them apart to be missionaries.

The world was turned upside down.

Antioch became the center from which the church would evangelize the known world.

Nearly a dozen new congregations were established throughout Asia by the work of these men.

Paul began a ministry of writing that gave us half of the New Testament.

Antioch was established as the central hub of Christianity in the ancient world.

My sincere prayer is that no church will be left behind in the greatest revival in the history of the Church. Personal and corporate prayer is the key.

Through the Holy Spirit, Jesus has placed this key in your hand!

Meditating on the Message

1. What do you have to do to get rid of the six circuit-breakers to answered prayer?

2. Why do fractured relationships with others affect our anointing with God?

3. What do you think are some hindrances to prayer in your own life?

Assignment: Does your church have an organized ministry of intercessory prayer? If yes, consider becoming a part of it. If no, consider organizing one.

ENDNOTES

Chapter 1

[1] James Rutz, *Megashift: Igniting Spiritual Power* (Colorado Springs: Empowerment, 2005) 15, 25, 40, 41, 45, 81, 82.

[2] George Barna, *The Second Coming of the Church* (Nashville: Word, 1998) 1.

[3] H. B. London and Neil B. Wiseman, *Pastors at Greater Risk* (Ventura, CA: Regal, 2003) 20, 172, 264.

Chapter 2

[1] Ken Houts research taken from lectures.

[2] J. Oswald Sanders, *Spiritual Leadership* (Chicago: Moody, 1994) 62.

[3] Sanders, 154.

[4] Dallas Willard, "Christian Disciplines as a Means to Grace," *Conversations: A Forum for Authentic Transformation*, Vol. 4:1, Spring 2006: 66.

[5] Dietrich Bonhoeffer, *The Cost of Discipleship* (New York: Macmillan, 1959) 35-36.

[6] Willard, 67.

Chapter 4

[1] Bill Hybels, *Just a Walk Across the Room: Simple Steps Pointing People to Faith* (Grand Rapids: Zondervan, 2006).

Chapter 5

1 Darrell W. Robinson, *Total Church Life* (Nashville: Broadman and Holman, 1997).

2 Rick Warren, *The Purpose Driven Church* (Grand Rapids: Zondervan, 1995).

3 George Barna, *The Frog in the Kettle* (Ventura, CA: Regal, 1990).

4 Mark Shaw, *Ten Great Ideas From Church History* (Downers Grove, IL: Intervarsity, 1997).

5 Leith Anderson, "Seven Ways to Rate Your Church," *Leadership* (Winter 1999).

6 Mark Dever, *Nine Marks of a Healthy Church* (Wheaton, IL: Crossway, 2004).

Chapter 7

1 Dr. Elmer Towns, *Knowing God Through Fasting* (Shippensburg, PA: Destiny Image, 2002).

2 Arthur Wallis, *God's Chosen Fast* (Fort Washington, PA: Christian Literature Crusade, 1968) 25-26.

3 Alton Garrison "Conversations: Tom Clegg," *Today's Pentecostal Evangel,* Aug. 27, 2006: 16.

4 Henry and Richard Blackaby, *Spiritual Leadership* (Broadman and Holman, 2001) 69.

5 Ed Stetzer and David Putnam, *Breaking the Missional Code: Your Church Can Become a Missionary in Your Community* (Nashville: Broadman and Holman, 2006) 22-27.

Chapter 8

[1] Dr. Leith Anderson, *Leadership That Works* (Minneapolis: Bethany House, 2002).

[2] Dr. Charles W. Conn, *Like a Mighty Army* (Cleveland, TN: Pathway, 1994).

[3] *Book of Minutes General Assemblies Church of God* (Cleveland, TN: Church of God Publishing House, 1922) 15-16.